Macmillan McGraw-Hill

Math Connects
5

Chapter 8
Resource Masters

Mc
Graw
Hill
Macmillan/McGraw-Hill

The McGraw·Hill Companies

 Macmillan/McGraw-Hill

Send all inquiries to:
Macmillan/McGraw-Hill
8787 Orion Place
Columbus, OH 43240-4027

ISBN: 978-0-02-107279-8
MHID: 0-02-107279-5

Chapter 8 Resource Masters

Printed in the United States of America.

3 4 5 6 7 8 9 10 005 16 15 14 13 12 11 10 09

Grade 5 Chapter 8
Table of Contents

Teacher's Guide to Using the
Chapter 8 Resource Masters

The *Chapter 8 Resource Masters* includes the core materials needed for Chapter 8. These materials include worksheets, extensions, and assessment options. The answers for these pages appear at the back of this booklet.

All of the materials found in this booklet are included for viewing and printing on the *TeacherWorks Plus*™ CD-ROM.

Chapter Resources

Graphic Organizer (page 1) This master is a tool designed to assist students with comprehension of grade-level concepts. While the content and layout of these tools vary, their goal is to assist students by providing a visual representation from which they can learn new concepts.

Student Glossary (page 2) This master is a study tool that presents the key vocabulary terms from the chapter. You may suggest that students highlight or star the terms they do not understand. Give this list to students before beginning Lesson 8–1. Remind them to add these pages to their mathematics study notebooks.

Anticipation Guide (page 6) This master is a survey designed for use before beginning the chapter. You can use this survey to highlight what students may or may not know about the concepts in the chapter. If feasible, interview students in small groups, asking them the interview questions in the guide. There is space for recording how well students answer the questions before they complete the chapter. You may find it helpful to interview students a second time, after completing the chapter, to determine their progress.

Game (page 7) A game is provided to reinforce chapter concepts and may be used at appropriate times throughout the chapter.

Resources for Computational Lessons

Reteach Each lesson has an associated Reteach worksheet. In general, the Reteach worksheet focuses on the same lesson content but uses a different approach, learning style, or modality than that used in the Student Edition. The Reteach worksheet closes with computational practice of the concept.

Skills Practice The Skills Practice worksheet for each lesson focuses on the computational aspect of the lesson. The Skills Practice worksheet may be helpful in providing additional practice of the skill taught in the lesson.

Homework Practice The Homework Practice worksheet provides an opportunity for additional computational practice. The Homework Practice worksheet includes word problems that address the skill taught in the lesson.

Problem-Solving Practice The Problem-Solving Practice worksheet presents additional reinforcement in solving word problems that apply both the concepts of the lesson and some review concepts.

Enrich The Enrich worksheet presents activities that extend the concepts of the lesson. Some Enrich materials are designed to widen students' perspectives on the mathematics they are learning. These worksheets are written for use with all levels of students.

Resources for Problem-Solving Strategy and Problem-Solving Investigation Lessons In recognition of the importance of problem-solving strategies, worksheets for problem-solving lessons follow a slightly different format. For problem-solving lessons, a two-page Reteach worksheet offers a complete model for choosing a problem-solving strategy. For each Problem-Solving Strategy lesson, Reteach and Homework Practice worksheets offer reinforcement of the strategy taught in the Student Edition lesson. In contrast, the Problem-Solving Investigation worksheets include a model strategy on the Reteach worksheets and provide problems requiring several alternate strategies on the Homework Practice and Skills Practice worksheets.

Assessment Options The assessment masters in the *Chapter 8 Resource Masters* offer a wide variety of assessment tools for monitoring progress as well as final assessment.

Individual Progress Checklist This checklist explains the chapter's goals or objectives. Teachers can record whether a student's mastery of each objective is beginning (B), developing (D), or mastered (M). The checklist includes space to record notes to parents as well as other pertinent observations.

Chapter Diagnostic Test This one-page test assesses students' grasp of skills that are needed for success in the chapter.

Chapter Pretest This one-page quick check of the chapter's concepts is useful for determining pacing. Performance on the pretest can help you determine which concepts can be covered quickly and which specific concepts may need additional time.

Quizzes Three free-response quizzes offer quick assessment opportunities at appropriate intervals in the chapter.

Mid-Chapter Test This one-page chapter test provides an option to assess the first half of the chapter. It includes both multiple-choice and free-response questions.

Vocabulary Test This one-page test focuses on chapter vocabulary. It is suitable for all students. It includes a list of vocabulary words and questions to assess students' knowledge of the words.

Oral Assessment Although this two-page assessment is designed to be used with all students, the interview format focuses on assessing chapter content assimilated by ELL students.

Chapter Project Rubric This one-page rubric is designed for use in assessing the chapter project. You may want to distribute copies of the rubric when you assign the project and use the rubric to record each student's chapter project score.

Foldables Rubric This one-page rubric is designed to assess the Foldables graphic organizer. The rubric is written to the students, telling them what you will be looking for as you evaluate their completed Foldables graphic organizer.

Leveled Chapter Tests

- **Form 1** assesses basic chapter concepts through multiple-choice questions and is designed for use with on-level students.

- **Form 2A** is designed for on-level students and is primarily for those who may have missed the Form 1 test. It may be used as a retest for students who received additional instruction following the Form 1 test.

- **Form 2B** is designed for students with a below-level command of the English language.

- **Form 2C** is a free-response test designed for on-level students.

- **Form 2D** is written for students with a below-level command of the English language.

- **Form 3** is a free-response test written for above-level students.

- **Extended-Response Test** is an extended response test for on-level students.

Cumulative Test Practice This three-page test, aimed at on-level students, offers multiple-choice questions and free-response questions.

Student Recording Sheet This one-page recording sheet is for the standardized test in the Student Edition.

Answers

The answers for the Anticipation Guide and Lesson Resources are provided as reduced pages with answers appearing in black. Full size line-up answer keys are provided for the Assessment Masters.

Name _____ Date _____

Graphic Organizer

Use this graphic organizer to take notes on Chapter 8: Develop Fraction Concepts. Fill in the missing information.

How do I ...	Instructions	Examples
... write a mixed number as an improper fraction?		
... rename an improper fraction as a mixed number?		
... use a number line to compare fractions?		
... round fractions?		

Name _____ Date _____

Student-Built Glossary

This is an alphabetical list of new vocabulary terms you will learn in **Chapter 8: Develop Fraction Concepts.** As you study the chapter, complete each term's definition or description. Remember to add the page number where you found the term. Add this page to your math study notebook to review vocabulary at the end of the chapter.

Vocabulary Term	Found on Page	Definition/Description/Example
denominator		
fraction		
improper fraction		
mixed number		
numerator		

MATH at HOME

Dear Family,

Today my class started **Chapter 8: Develop Fraction Concepts.** I will be learning to generate equivalent mixed numbers and improper fractions. I will also be learning to round fractions and mixed numbers and compare fractions. Here are my vocabulary words and an activity that we can do together.

Sincerely, _____

Key Vocabulary

Fraction: A number that represents part of a whole or part of a set. Example: $\frac{1}{2}$, $\frac{1}{3}$, $\frac{1}{4}$, and $\frac{3}{4}$ are fractions.

Numerator: The number above the bar in a fraction; the part of the fraction that tells how many of the equal parts are being used. Example: $\frac{2}{4}$, 2 is the numerator.

Denominator: The bottom number in a fraction. Example: $\frac{5}{6}$, 6 is the denominator.

Improper fraction: A fraction that has a numerator that is greater than or equal to its denominator. Example: $\frac{29}{5}$.

Mixed number: A number that has a whole number and a fraction. Example: $1\frac{3}{4}$

Activity

Sort marbles according to color. Create fractions, using the different marble colors to represent parts of the whole amount of marbles. Draw a pizza pie in the middle of a piece of poster paper and divide your pie into the number of marbles for each color. Practice adding together different sets of fractions.

Books to Read

Polar Bear Math, Learning About Fractions
by Nagda and Bickel

The Doorbell Rang
by Pat Hutchins

Gator Pie
by Louise Mathews

-Hill, a division of The McGraw-Hill Companies, Inc.

MATEMÁTICAS en CASA

Estimada familia:

Hoy mi clase comenzó el **Capítulo 8: Desarrolla conceptos de fracción**. Aprenderé a sumar y a restar fracciones. También aprenderé a redondear fracciones y números mixtos. A continuación, están mis palabras del vocabulario y una actividad que podemos realizar juntos.

Sinceramente, _____

Vocabulario clave

fracción Número que representa parte de un todo o parte de un conjunto. Ejemplo: $\frac{1}{2}$, $\frac{1}{3}$, $\frac{1}{4}$ y $\frac{3}{4}$ son fracciones.

numerador Número que está encima de la barra de fracción; la parte de la fracción que indica cuántas partes iguales se están usando. Ejemplo: En $\frac{2}{4}$, 2 es el numerador.

denominador El número inferior en una fracción. Ejemplo: En $\frac{5}{6}$, 6 es el denominador.

fracción impropia Fracción cuyo numerador es mayor que o igual a su denominador. Ejemplo: $\frac{29}{5}$.

número mixto Número compuesto por un número entero y una fracción. Ejemplo: $1\frac{3}{4}$.

Actividad

Clasifiquen canicas según sus colores. Creen fracciones a partir de los colores (partes) y de la cantidad de canicas (todo). Dibujen una pizza redonda en el centro de una cartulina y divídanla según el número de canicas por color. Practiquen a sumar los distintos conjuntos de fracciones.

Libros recomendados

Matemáticas de osos polares: Aprende sobre fracciones
de Nagda and Bickel

Sonó el timbre
de Pat Hutchins

Pastel de cocodrilo
de Louise Mathews

8

Anticipation Guide

Develop Fraction Concepts

STEP 1 *Before you begin Chapter 8*

- Read each statement.

- Decide whether you agree (A) or disagree (D) with the statement.

- Write A or D in the first column OR if you are not sure whether you agree or disagree, write NS (not sure).

STEP 1 A, D, or NS	Statement	STEP 2 A or D
	1. $\frac{10}{9}$ is an improper fraction.	
	2. A fraction means to divide.	
	3. A mixed number has a whole number and a fraction.	
	4. $\frac{7}{12}$ is an improper fraction.	
	5. A fraction is a number that represents part of a whole or part of a set.	
	6. $\frac{11}{3}$ is a mixed number.	
	7. An improper fraction is converted to a mixed number by multiplying and adding.	
	8. In the fraction $\frac{6}{10}$, 10 is the denominator.	
	9. In the fraction $\frac{3}{12}$, 3 is the denominator.	
	10. In the fraction $\frac{3}{4}$, 3 is the numerator.	

STEP 2 *After you complete Chapter 8*

- Reread each statement and complete the last column by entering an A (agree) or a D (disagree).

- Did any of your opinions about the statements change from the first column?

- For those statements that you mark with a D, use a separate sheet of paper to explain why you disagree. Use examples, if possible.

8

Game
Change That Fraction

You will need
- 2 pairs of number cubes
- Paper and pencil

Give each player a pair of number cubes, paper, and pencil.

GO!

1. Have each player toss her or his number cubes and form a proper fraction with the numbers tossed on the cubes.

2. Each player rounds his or her fraction to 0, $\frac{1}{2}$, or 1 and receives that amount as the point total.

3. Continue the activity as each player adds their rounded amounts.

4. The first player to reach 10 points wins.

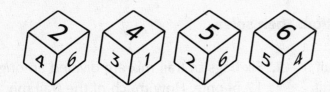

Name _____ Date _____

Reteach

Fractions and Division

Kelly, Jose, Jason, and Melanie are sharing 1 pizza. How much pizza does each person get?

A **fraction** is a number that names equal parts of a whole or parts of a group. A fraction represents division. If 1 is divided into 4 equal parts, one part is $\frac{1}{4}$.

The **numerator** is the number above the bar in a fraction.	The **denominator** is the number below the bar in a fraction.

Words: 1 pizza divided among 4 people
Symbols: 1 ÷ 4

Fraction:

1 pizza   → 1 ← numerator
4 people → $\overline{4}$ ← denominator

Model:

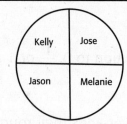

The fraction $\frac{1}{4}$ means that each person gets $\frac{1}{4}$ of the pizza.

Represent each situation using a fraction. Then solve.

1. At the picnic there are 3 pieces of fruit for 4 people. How many pieces of fruit will each person receive?

_____

_____

_____

2. Six bags of trail mix are divided among 17 people. How much of the trail mix did each person receive?

_____

_____

_____

8

Name _____ Date _____

Skills Practice

Fractions and Division

Represent each situation using a fraction. Then solve.

1. Mr. Janson has 3 jars of soup to divide among 4 people. How much soup will each person receive?

   _____

   _____

2. Andrew shares his suitcase with his two brothers on vacation. How much space in the suitcase will Andrew and his brothers each have?

   _____

   _____

3. Two small pizzas are shared by three people. How much pizza does each person get?

   _____

   _____

4. One container of paint is used to paint 7 tables. How much paint did each table use?

   _____

   _____

5. Five cupcakes are divided among 4 people. How many cupcakes does each person get?

   _____

   _____

6. Four loaves of bread are divided equally among three students. How much bread will each student get?

   _____

   _____

Name _____   Date _____

Homework Practice

Fractions and Division

Represent each situation using a fraction. Then solve.

1. Three bags of soil are used to fill 4 flowerpots. How many cups of soil does each flowerpot use?

   _____

2. Three people equally share five lemon squares. How many lemon squares does each person receive?

   _____

3. In science class there are 5 cups of water to be used for the experiments. If six students work on the experiments, how many cups of water does each student receive?

   _____

4. Four yards of fabric are used to make five craft projects. How many yards of fabric does each craft project use?

   _____

Spiral Review

Which type of graph would you use to display the data in each table? Write bar graph, line graph, or pictograph.

5. Brandon surveyed his classmates to find their favorite sport. Which type of graph should you use to display the data? Which sport is most popular?

Favorite Sports	
Basketball	9
Baseball	6
Football	18
Soccer	7
Lacrosse	3

6. The following table shows the height of five students. Which type of graph should you use? What is the median of these heights?

Student Heights	
Name	Height (in.)
Jennifer	58
Troy	55
Bianca	49
Rosa	50
Anna	42

Problem-Solving Practice

Fractions and Division

Represent each situation using a fraction. Then solve.

1. Elena drank 5 bottles of water over 7 days. How much water did Elena drink each day?

_____

2. Molly is slicing 3 pizzas into equal slices so that 8 people can each have a piece. How much pizza does each person receive?

_____

3. The Littleton family drinks 2 gallons of milk in 5 days. How many gallons do they drink each day?

_____

4. Three gallons of paint are used to paint 16 wooden signs. How much paint did each sign use?

_____

5. Three bags of packing peanuts are used to fill 2 boxes. How many bags of packing peanuts does each box use?

_____

6. Nine yards of ribbon are used to make 2 bows. How many yards of ribbon does each bow use?

_____

11

Name _____ Date _____

Enrich

Fractions and Division

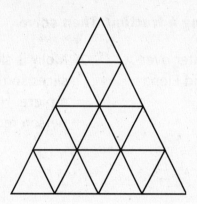

1. The large triangle is made of four rows of small triangles. Some of the small triangles have three corners that are on the large triangle. Shade each of these small triangles.

2. Some of the triangles have exactly two corners that are on the large triangle. Draw a dot in each of these small triangles.

3. Some of the triangles have exactly one corner that is on the large triangle. Draw an X in each of these small triangles.

4. Some of the triangles have no corners that are on the large triangle. Draw a star in each of these small triangles.

5. What fraction of the small triangles is shaded?

_____

6. What fraction of the small triangles has a dot?

_____

7. What fraction of the small triangles has an X?

_____

8. What fraction of the small triangles has a star?

_____

9. What fraction of the small triangles has at least one corner that is on the larger triangle?

_____

Name _____ Date _____

Reteach

Improper Fractions

An **improper fraction** is a fraction that has a numerator that is greater than or equal to its denominator.	A **mixed number** has a whole number and a fraction.
Example: $\dfrac{7}{4}$ $\dfrac{8}{6}$ $\dfrac{9}{2}$ $\dfrac{2}{2}$	Example: $5\dfrac{1}{3}$ $3\dfrac{1}{2}$ $6\dfrac{2}{5}$

Renaming an Improper Fraction

To write an improper fraction as a mixed number, divide the numerator by the denominator. Write the remainder as a fraction of the divisor.

Example: $\dfrac{8}{3} = \begin{array}{r} 2R2 \\ 3\overline{)8} \\ -6 \\ \hline 2 \end{array} \rightarrow 2\dfrac{2}{3}$ Example: $\dfrac{19}{4} = \begin{array}{r} 4R3 \\ 4\overline{)19} \\ -16 \\ \hline 3 \end{array} \rightarrow 4\dfrac{3}{4}$

Write each improper fraction as a mixed number.

1. $\dfrac{15}{2}$ _____

2. $\dfrac{18}{5}$ _____

3. $\dfrac{9}{4}$ _____

4. $\dfrac{4}{3}$ _____

5. $\dfrac{7}{2}$ _____

6. $\dfrac{19}{6}$ _____

7. $\dfrac{17}{2}$ _____

8. $\dfrac{9}{8}$ _____

9. $\dfrac{13}{2}$ _____

10. $\dfrac{7}{4}$ _____

11. $\dfrac{27}{7}$ _____

12. $\dfrac{29}{8}$ _____

13. $\dfrac{23}{3}$ _____

14. $\dfrac{33}{5}$ _____

15. $\dfrac{19}{2}$ _____

Name _____ Date _____

Skills Practice

Improper Fractions

Write each improper fraction as a mixed number.

1. $\dfrac{13}{2}$ _____

2. $\dfrac{5}{3}$ _____

3. $\dfrac{19}{3}$ _____

4. $\dfrac{3}{2}$ _____

5. $\dfrac{17}{4}$ _____

6. $\dfrac{31}{5}$ _____

7. $\dfrac{16}{5}$ _____

8. $\dfrac{4}{3}$ _____

9. $\dfrac{13}{9}$ _____

10. $\dfrac{11}{3}$ _____

11. $\dfrac{49}{8}$ _____

12. $\dfrac{8}{5}$ _____

13. $\dfrac{44}{9}$ _____

14. $\dfrac{12}{11}$ _____

15. $\dfrac{38}{7}$ _____

16. $\dfrac{20}{7}$ _____

17. $\dfrac{41}{8}$ _____

18. $\dfrac{10}{7}$ _____

19. $\dfrac{19}{5}$ _____

20. $\dfrac{7}{3}$ _____

21. $\dfrac{29}{9}$ _____

22. $\dfrac{51}{8}$ _____

23. $\dfrac{17}{6}$ _____

24. $\dfrac{9}{2}$ _____

25. $\dfrac{45}{8}$ _____

26. $\dfrac{68}{7}$ _____

27. $\dfrac{12}{5}$ _____

28. $\dfrac{22}{3}$ _____

29. $\dfrac{49}{6}$ _____

30. $\dfrac{28}{3}$ _____

Name _____ Date _____

Homework Practice

Improper Fractions

Write each improper fraction as a mixed number.

1. $\frac{11}{6}$ _____

2. $\frac{13}{4}$ _____

3. $\frac{41}{7}$ _____

4. $\frac{19}{4}$ _____

5. $\frac{5}{2}$ _____

6. $\frac{38}{5}$ _____

7. $\frac{9}{2}$ _____

8. $\frac{14}{3}$ _____

9. $\frac{39}{8}$ _____

10. $\frac{25}{6}$ _____

11. $\frac{22}{5}$ _____

12. $\frac{17}{4}$ _____

13. $\frac{80}{9}$ _____

14. $\frac{13}{10}$ _____

15. $\frac{67}{7}$ _____

16. $\frac{71}{8}$ _____

17. $\frac{8}{3}$ _____

18. $\frac{14}{5}$ _____

19. $\frac{28}{3}$ _____

20. $\frac{61}{7}$ _____

21. $\frac{13}{6}$ _____

Spiral Review

Represent each situation using a fraction. Then solve. (Lesson 8–1)

22. Eight people equally share 3 pizzas. How much pizza does each person recieve?

_____

23. In art class, there are 5 sheets of drawing paper for 9 people. How much paper will each person receive?

_____

24. Five gallons of punch fill 3 punch bowls equally. How much punch will be in each punch bowl?

_____

8-2

Problem-Solving Practice

Improper Fractions

Solve.

1. Sixty-three students have signed up for summer soccer camp. If each soccer team can have 11 players, how many teams can be formed? Write the answer as a mixed number and as a remainder. Explain what the remainder means.

_____

2. Taye rode his bicycle 47 miles in 3 hours. Write the number of miles ridden each hour as a mixed number.

_____

3. Shawna is decorating a scrapbook page with stickers. She has 40 stickers and 6 stickers will fit on one scrapbook page. How many pages can she fill with stickers? Write the answer as a mixed number and as a remainder. Explain what the remainder means.

_____

4. Rodney is putting away test tubes in science class. He has 50 test tubes and 12 will fit on each rack. How many racks will Rodney fill? Write the answer as a mixed number.

_____

5. Leah is assembling gift bags for her birthday party. Nine friends are coming to the party. Leah has 58 items for all the gift bags. How many items should she put in each bag? Will there be any items left over?

_____

6. Arvin is making a fruit snack for himself and his 3 brothers. If he has 35 apple slices, how many will each brother get? Write the answer as a mixed number and as a remainder. Explain what the remainder means.

_____

Name _____ Date _____

Enrich

Understanding Fractions

Match each improper fraction below a blank to a mixed number with a letter below. Write the letter in the blank to complete a quote by Willy Wonka from the book *Charlie and the Chocolate Factory* by Roald Dahl.

"A little nonsense now and then

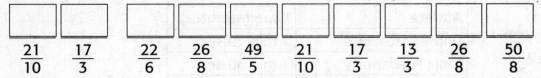

$\frac{21}{10}$ $\frac{17}{3}$ $\frac{22}{6}$ $\frac{26}{8}$ $\frac{49}{5}$ $\frac{21}{10}$ $\frac{17}{3}$ $\frac{13}{3}$ $\frac{26}{8}$ $\frac{50}{8}$

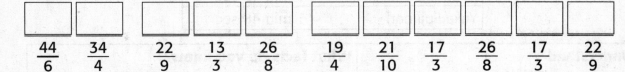

$\frac{44}{6}$ $\frac{34}{4}$ $\frac{22}{9}$ $\frac{13}{3}$ $\frac{26}{8}$ $\frac{19}{4}$ $\frac{21}{10}$ $\frac{17}{3}$ $\frac{26}{8}$ $\frac{17}{3}$ $\frac{22}{9}$

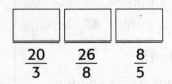

$\frac{20}{3}$ $\frac{26}{8}$ $\frac{8}{5}$

$N = 1\frac{3}{5}$ $S = 5\frac{2}{3}$ $I = 2\frac{1}{10}$ $D = 6\frac{2}{8}$

$M = 6\frac{2}{3}$ $W = 4\frac{3}{4}$ $H = 4\frac{1}{3}$ $T = 2\frac{4}{9}$

$E = 3\frac{2}{8}$ $L = 9\frac{4}{5}$ $R = 3\frac{4}{6}$ $Y = 8\frac{2}{4}$

$B = 7\frac{2}{6}$

How did you change $3\frac{2}{8}$ into an improper fraction?

_____

_____

_____

Name _____ Date _____

Reteach

Problem-Solving Strategy: Use Logical Reasoning

Use the logical reasoning strategy to solve problems.

The table shows the times of some women who competed in the Snowboard Cross event in the 2006 Winter Olympics. How much less time did it take Tanja Freiden than Yuka Fujimori?

Athlete	Time (minutes)
Lindsey Jacobellis	1 min 29 sec
Tanja Frieden	1 min 30 sec
Katharina Himmler	1 min 43 sec
Yuka Fujimori	1 min 48 sec

Understand	**What facts do you know?** Tanja Frieden's time was 1 minute 30 seconds. Yuka Fujimori's time was 1 minute 48 seconds. **What do you need to find?** How much less time it took Tanja Frieden than it took Yuka Fujimori.
Plan	You can subtract 1 minute 30 seconds from 1 minute 48 seconds to find the answer.
Solve	**Use your plan to solve the problem.** 1 min 48 sec − 1 min 30 sec = 18 sec
Check	Look back. 1 minute 30 seconds + 18 seconds = 1 minute 48 seconds. So, you know the answer is correct.

Solve. Use logical reasoning.

1. Miss Graham's class is buying supplies for a party. They need to buy 3 packs of balloons, 2 rolls of streamers, and 1 set of wall decorations. Use the chart below to find out how much each item costs. How much will their party supplies cost in all?

Item	Cost
Pack of Balloons	$1.37
Roll of Streamers	$0.99
Set of Wall Decorations	$8.50

18

Name _____ Date _____

Reteach

Use Logical Reasoning (continued)

Solve. Use logical reasoning.

2. Barbara can swim four laps in 2 minutes. How long does it take her to swim one lap?

_____

3. The park has 3 more maple trees than spruce trees. There are 13 maple and spruce trees in all. How many maple trees are there?

_____

4. Leonard can run a mile in 9 minutes. Alicia can run a mile in 7 minutes. If they run together, how long after Alicia finishes will Leonard finish?

_____

5. Carl is making a garden. He buys 3 packets of violet seeds for $0.35 each, 2 packets of marigold seeds for $0.50 each, one bag of soil for $1.50, and a new pair of gloves for $4.50. How much money will Carl spend in all?

_____

6. Ramona can ride her bike 1 mile in 5 minutes. How long will it take her to ride 4 miles?

_____

7. Ronald and his brother are going to visit their grandmother. If their father drives 45 miles an hour, it will take 2 hours to get there. How far do they have to travel?

_____

8-3

Skills Practice

Problem-Solving Strategy

Solve. Use logical reasoning.

1. Julia can make 2 pieces of toast in 3 minutes. How long will it take her to make 8 pieces of toast?

_____

2. Jeff has saved $40.50. He wants to buy a new pair of shoes which cost $35.75. The sales tax on these shoes is $2.50. How much money will Jeff have left over after making this purchase?

_____

3. In the school choir there are 3 more boys than girls. There are 13 boys and girls in the choir in all. How many boys are there in the choir?

_____

4. The following chart shows some of the countries who earned the most gold medals in the 2006 Winter Olympics. How many more medals did Austria win than Estonia?

Country	Number of Gold Medals
Germany	11
Austria	9
South Korea	6
Estonia	3

5. Louise, Jacqueline, and Martha ran a one-mile race. Louise finished in 8.47 minutes, Jacqueline finished in 9.32 minutes, and Martha finished in 8.34 minutes. How much time passed between Martha's finish and Jacqueline's finish?

_____

6. Shamera and Diana have played 14 games of checkers. Shamera has won 2 more games than Diana. How many games has Diana won?

_____

Name _____ Date _____

Homework Practice

Problem-Solving Strategy

Solve. Use logical reasoning.

1. For a science lesson, Mr. Miller asked his students to each bring in a leaf or a pinecone. The students brought in 21 leaves and pinecones in all. There were 5 more leaves than pinecones. How many pinecones did the students bring in?

   _____

2. Jenna can swim one lap in the pool in 36 seconds. How long will it take her to swim 3 laps?

   _____

3. There are 16 ounces in 1 pound. How many ounces are there in 3 pounds?

   _____

4. Marcus is practicing for the basketball team. The chart below shows the number of minutes he has practiced for each of the last 4 days. If the pattern continues, how many minutes will he practice on the fifth day?

   _____

Day	Time (in minutes)
One	30
Two	45
Three	60
Four	75
Five	_____

Spiral Review

Write each improper fraction as a mixed number. (Lesson 8–2)

5. $\frac{7}{2}$ _____

6. $\frac{5}{3}$ _____

7. $\frac{12}{5}$ _____

8. $\frac{15}{2}$ _____

9. $\frac{18}{7}$ _____

10. $\frac{9}{4}$ _____

Name _____ Date _____

Enrich

Egyptian Fractions

The ancient Egyptians wrote numbers using different symbols than those we use today. The ancient Egyptian symbols for 100, 10, and 1 are shown below.

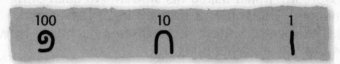

The Egyptian symbol for the number 215 is shown at the right.

A *unit fraction* has 1 as its numerator. Ancient Egyptians wrote all fraction as unit fractions. To show a fraction, they used the symbol for a mouth ⬭ above the denominator. The ancient Egyptian symbol for $\frac{1}{12}$ is shown at the right.

Write the ancient Egyptian symbol for each number.

1. 16

2. 24

3. 131

_____   _____   _____

Write the ancient Egyptian symbol for each fraction.

4. $\frac{1}{3}$

5. $\frac{1}{10}$

6. $\frac{1}{17}$

_____   _____   _____

7. $\frac{1}{25}$

8. $\frac{1}{110}$

9. $\frac{1}{201}$

_____   _____   _____

Write each Eyptian fraction as it would be written today.

10.

11.

12.

13.

_____   _____   _____   _____

Name _____ Date _____

Reteach

Mixed Numbers

Chapter Resources

A **mixed number** is made up of a whole number and a fraction.
An **improper fraction** is a fraction in which the numerator is greater than or equal to the denominator.

Write $2\frac{2}{3}$ as an improper fraction.

Step 1
Multiply the whole number by the denominator.

$2\frac{2}{3} \longrightarrow 2 \times 3 = 6$

Step 2
Add the numerator to the product.

$6 + 2 = 8$

Step 3
Write the sum over the denominator.

$2\frac{2}{3} = \frac{8}{3}$

Write each mixed number as an improper fraction.

1. $2\frac{2}{7}$ _____

2. $5\frac{3}{4}$ _____

3. $6\frac{5}{8}$ _____

4. $3\frac{4}{10}$ _____

5. $9\frac{1}{3}$ _____

6. $4\frac{4}{5}$ _____

7. $1\frac{1}{8}$ _____

8. $3\frac{1}{2}$ _____

9. $2\frac{2}{5}$ _____

10. $2\frac{2}{3}$ _____

11. $1\frac{3}{4}$ _____

12. $1\frac{1}{5}$ _____

13. $6\frac{2}{3}$ _____

14. $3\frac{2}{5}$ _____

15. $4\frac{1}{2}$ _____

16. $1\frac{4}{5}$ _____

17. $3\frac{5}{8}$ _____

18. $2\frac{2}{3}$ _____

Name _____ Date _____

Skills Practice

Mixed Numbers

Write each mixed number as an improper fraction.

1. $3\frac{1}{2}$ _____

2. $5\frac{3}{4}$ _____

3. $6\frac{7}{8}$ _____

4. $5\frac{5}{12}$ _____

5. $4\frac{1}{6}$ _____

6. $6\frac{2}{3}$ _____

7. $12\frac{2}{3}$ _____

8. $10\frac{23}{100}$ _____

9. $9\frac{1}{4}$ _____

10. $8\frac{2}{5}$ _____

11. $25\frac{1}{4}$ _____

12. $22\frac{1}{2}$ _____

13. $6\frac{4}{5}$ _____

14. $4\frac{3}{10}$ _____

15. $6\frac{1}{100}$ _____

16. $7\frac{5}{8}$ _____

17. $6\frac{3}{8}$ _____

18. $3\frac{9}{100}$ _____

19. $5\frac{5}{6}$ _____

20. $9\frac{3}{17}$ _____

21. $25\frac{1}{3}$ _____

22. $5\frac{2}{9}$ _____

23. $12\frac{2}{3}$ _____

24. $5\frac{3}{7}$ _____

25. $6\frac{4}{9}$ _____

26. $10\frac{1}{18}$ _____

27. $5\frac{5}{12}$ _____

28. $6\frac{2}{13}$ _____

29. $25\frac{4}{5}$ _____

30. $20\frac{5}{6}$ _____

Solve.

31. Tina spent $3\frac{1}{3}$ hours practicing the piano. Write this quantity as an improper fraction.

_____

32. Suppose you have $2\frac{1}{4}$ oranges. Write this quantity as an improper fraction.

_____

Name _____ Date _____

Homework Practice

Mixed Numbers

Write each mixed number as an improper fraction.

1. $2\frac{3}{4}$ _____

2. $5\frac{1}{6}$ _____

3. $8\frac{1}{2}$ _____

4. $3\frac{2}{3}$ _____

5. $7\frac{2}{5}$ _____

6. $1\frac{9}{10}$ _____

7. $4\frac{7}{8}$ _____

8. $6\frac{5}{7}$ _____

9. $1\frac{8}{9}$ _____

10. $3\frac{12}{17}$ _____

11. $2\frac{1}{10}$ _____

12. $5\frac{5}{13}$ _____

13. $1\frac{1}{2}$ _____

14. $7\frac{1}{3}$ _____

15. 3 _____

16. $3\frac{1}{2}$ _____

17. $4\frac{2}{3}$ _____

18. 8 _____

19. $2\frac{3}{5}$ _____

20. $5\frac{3}{4}$ _____

21. $2\frac{5}{8}$ _____

22. $1\frac{29}{35}$ _____

23. $6\frac{1}{3}$ _____

24. $5\frac{1}{2}$ _____

25. $3\frac{7}{10}$ _____

26. $4\frac{1}{2}$ _____

27. $4\frac{1}{10}$ _____

28. $5\frac{2}{5}$ _____

29. $8\frac{3}{4}$ _____

30. $2\frac{3}{5}$ _____

Spiral Review

Solve. Use logical reasoning.

31. A shipment of boxes weighs 40 pounds. There are 8 boxes and each weighs the same number of pounds. How much does each box weigh?

32. Mrs. Cooper's fifth-grade class has 11 more girls than boys. There are 35 students in all. How many girls are there?

_____   _____

Name _____ Date _____

Problem-Solving Practice

Mixed Numbers

Solve.

1. During the holiday break, Anthony read one book, and half of another book. How many books did he read?

2. Sam's family ate 2 pizzas. Then they ate 5 of the 8 slices of another pizza. How many pizzas did his family eat?

3. Hans ran 3 miles on the track. He took a break, then ran another $\frac{4}{5}$ mile. Write the number of miles Hans ran as an improper fraction.

4. Lindsey ran in a 10-kilometer race. This is equal to $6\frac{1}{5}$ miles. Write the number of miles Lindsey ran as an improper fraction.

5. Keisha is running on an indoor track where 8 laps equals one mile. If she runs 19 laps, how many miles is this? Write your answer as a mixed number and as an improper fraction.

6. Doug found that it takes 20 minutes to do 8 math problems. If he has 28 problems, how long will it take him to do them?

Name _____   Date _____

Enrich

A Maze of Mixed Numbers

Solve A–N by rounding to the nearest whole number. Then find your way through the maze to reach the dot. When you come to a letter, choose the number that matches your answer. Follow the path until you reach the next intersection.

A. $2\frac{7}{8}$ _____   **B.** $6\frac{1}{7}$ _____   **C.** $3\frac{3}{4}$ _____   **D.** $8\frac{2}{10}$ _____

E. $9\frac{7}{9}$ _____   **F.** $\frac{5}{6}$ _____   **G.** $12\frac{5}{7}$ _____   **H.** $20\frac{5}{7}$ _____

I. $18\frac{2}{10}$ _____   **J.** $16\frac{7}{9}$ _____   **K.** $7\frac{3}{20}$ _____   **L.** $1\frac{4}{5}$ _____

M. $5\frac{2}{14}$ _____   **N.** $14\frac{8}{10}$ _____

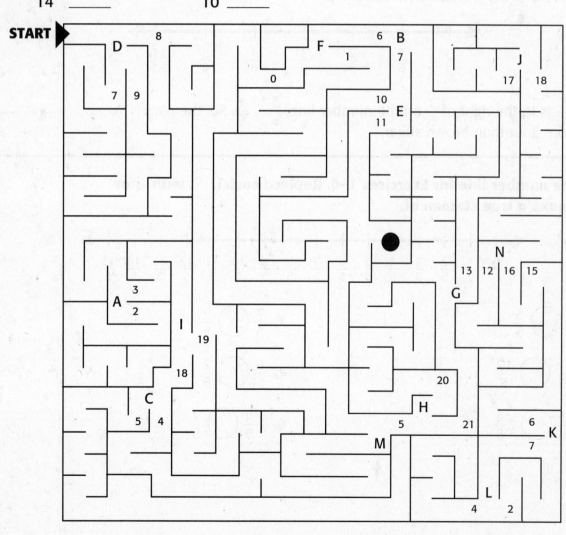

Name _____ Date _____

Reteach

Fractions on a Number Line

Giselle is making a recipe that calls for $\frac{1}{6}$ cup of brown sugar and $\frac{5}{6}$ cup of flour. Does the recipe have more brown sugar or flour?

You can see from the models that $\frac{1}{6} < \frac{5}{6}$.

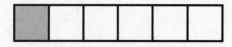

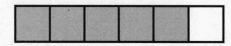

You can also use number lines to compare fractions.
There are 6 equal sections between 0 and 1.

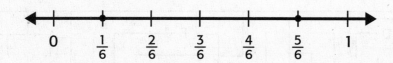

Since $\frac{5}{6}$ is to the right of $\frac{1}{6}$ on the number line, $\frac{5}{6} > \frac{1}{6}$. So, the recipe has more flour than brown sugar.

Use the number line for Exercises 1–6. Replace each ◯ with < or > to make a true statement.

1. $\frac{1}{5}$ ◯ $\frac{3}{5}$

2. $\frac{7}{5}$ ◯ $\frac{2}{5}$

3. $2\frac{1}{5}$ ◯ $\frac{12}{5}$

4. $\frac{6}{5}$ ◯ $\frac{2}{5}$

5. $\frac{13}{5}$ ◯ $2\frac{4}{5}$

6. $1\frac{4}{5}$ ◯ $\frac{7}{5}$

Name _____ Date _____

Skills Practice

Fractions on a Number Line

Use the number line for Exercises 1–6. Replace each ◯ with < or > to make a true statement.

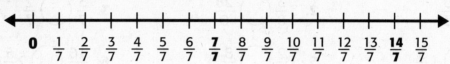

0 $\frac{1}{7}$ $\frac{2}{7}$ $\frac{3}{7}$ $\frac{4}{7}$ $\frac{5}{7}$ $\frac{6}{7}$ $\mathbf{\frac{7}{7}}$ $\frac{8}{7}$ $\frac{9}{7}$ $\frac{10}{7}$ $\frac{11}{7}$ $\frac{12}{7}$ $\frac{13}{7}$ $\mathbf{\frac{14}{7}}$ $\frac{15}{7}$

1. $\frac{1}{7}$ ◯ $\frac{3}{7}$

2. $\frac{6}{7}$ ◯ $\frac{4}{7}$

3. $1\frac{1}{7}$ ◯ $\frac{14}{7}$

4. $\frac{9}{7}$ ◯ $\frac{2}{7}$

5. $\frac{11}{7}$ ◯ $2\frac{1}{7}$

6. $1\frac{2}{7}$ ◯ $\frac{8}{7}$

Replace each ◯ with < or > to make a true statement.

7. $\frac{2}{4}$ ◯ $\frac{3}{4}$

8. $1\frac{1}{9}$ ◯ $\frac{8}{9}$

9. $\frac{5}{6}$ ◯ $\frac{2}{6}$

10. $\frac{9}{10}$ ◯ $\frac{2}{10}$

11. $1\frac{2}{8}$ ◯ $\frac{11}{8}$

12. $\frac{14}{7}$ ◯ $2\frac{3}{7}$

13. $\frac{9}{5}$ ◯ $1\frac{3}{5}$

14. $\frac{7}{11}$ ◯ $\frac{6}{11}$

15. $\frac{10}{4}$ ◯ $2\frac{1}{4}$

Write the fraction or mixed number that is represented by each point.

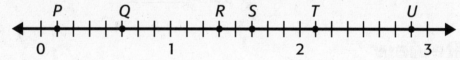

P   Q   R S   T   U
0   1   2   3

16. P _____

17. Q _____

18. R _____

19. S _____

20. T _____

21. U _____

Solve.

22. Amelia's bookshelf is $\frac{3}{5}$ full of books and $\frac{1}{5}$ full of magazines. Does her bookshelf have more books or magazines? Explain.

_____

Name _____ Date _____

Homework Practice

Fractions on a Number Line

Replace each ◯ with < or > to make a true statement.

1. $\frac{2}{3}$ ◯ $\frac{5}{3}$

2. $3\frac{3}{8}$ ◯ $\frac{28}{8}$

3. $\frac{3}{7}$ ◯ $\frac{2}{7}$

4. $\frac{11}{9}$ ◯ $1\frac{3}{9}$

5. $1\frac{2}{5}$ ◯ $\frac{8}{5}$

6. $\frac{16}{7}$ ◯ $2\frac{5}{7}$

7. $\frac{9}{4}$ ◯ $1\frac{3}{4}$

8. $\frac{13}{10}$ ◯ $1\frac{1}{10}$

9. $\frac{13}{8}$ ◯ $2\frac{1}{8}$

Write the fraction or mixed number that is represented by each point.

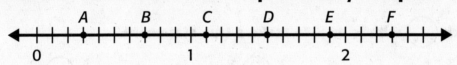

10. A _____

11. B _____

12. C _____

13. D _____

14. E _____

15. F _____

Spiral Review

Write each mixed number as an improper fraction. (Lesson 8–4)

16. $2\frac{3}{5}$ _____

17. $5\frac{1}{10}$ _____

18. $4\frac{5}{8}$ _____

19. $11\frac{4}{5}$ _____

20. $6\frac{1}{7}$ _____

21. $7\frac{2}{9}$ _____

Name _____ Date _____

Problem-Solving Practice

Fractions on a Number Line

Solve.

1. James walks $2\frac{1}{7}$ miles to school. Kiana walks $\frac{19}{7}$ miles to school. Who walks farther to school? Explain.

_____

2. Clarice lives $\frac{17}{8}$ miles from her grandmother's house and $2\frac{3}{8}$ miles from her aunt's house. Does Clarice live closer to her aunt or her grandmother? Explain.

_____

3. Henry's pet bird weighs $4\frac{3}{16}$ ounces and his pet kitten weighs $\frac{65}{16}$ ounces. Which pet weighs more? Explain.

_____

_____

4. A recipe for lemonade calls for $\frac{11}{4}$ cup lemon juice and $2\frac{1}{4}$ cup water. Does the recipe have more lemon juice or water? Explain.

_____

_____

5. Elina made a skirt using $3\frac{2}{5}$ yards of fabric. She made a dress using $\frac{17}{5}$ yards of fabric. Which item used more fabric? Explain.

_____

_____

6. Greg's dad planted $5\frac{2}{9}$ rows of his garden with lettuce. He planted $\frac{42}{9}$ rows of the garden with carrots. Did he plant more lettuce or carrots? Explain.

_____

_____

Name _____ Date _____

Enrich

Unit Rates

A **unit rate** is a comparison of two quantities by division in which the denominator is 1.

Description	Rate	Unit Rate
riding a bicycle 23 miles in 2 hours	$\dfrac{23 \text{ miles}}{2 \text{ hours}}$	$\dfrac{23 \text{ miles} \div 2}{2 \text{ hours} \div 2} = \dfrac{11\frac{1}{2} \text{ miles}}{1 \text{ hour}}$ $= 11\frac{1}{2} \text{ miles/hour}$
reading 14 pages in 8 minutes	$\dfrac{14 \text{ pages}}{8 \text{ minutes}}$	$\dfrac{14 \text{ pages} \div 8}{8 \text{ minutes} \div 8} = \dfrac{1\frac{3}{4} \text{ pages}}{1 \text{ minute}}$ $= 1\frac{3}{4} \text{ pages/minute}$
earning $33 for babysitting 5 hours	$\dfrac{\$33}{5 \text{ hours}}$	$\dfrac{\$33 \div 5}{5 \text{ hours} \div 5} = \dfrac{\$6.60}{1 \text{ hour}}$ $= \$6.60/\text{hour}$

Find each unit rate.

1. 52 gallons of water for 5 fish _____

2. typing 111 words in 2 minutes _____

3. canoeing 49 miles in 4 days _____

4. a total weight of 78 pounds for 9 boxes _____

5. earning $350 for working 40 hours _____

6. An SUV can go 230 miles on one tank of gas. The gas tank holds 25 gallons. What is the SUV's gas mileage in miles per gallon? _____

7. A messenger delivers 8 packages in 3 hours. At that rate, how many packages can she deliver in 15 hours? _____

Name _____ Date _____

Reteach

Round Fractions

Round Up

If the numerator is almost as large as the denominator, round the number up to the next whole number.

Example: $\frac{9}{10}$ rounds to 1.

9 is almost as large as 10.

Round to $\frac{1}{2}$

If the numerator is about half of the denominator, round the fraction to $\frac{1}{2}$.

Example: $\frac{3}{5}$ rounds to $\frac{1}{2}$.

3 is about half of 5.

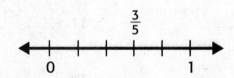

Round Down

If the numerator is much smaller than the denominator, round the number down to the previous whole number.

Example: $\frac{1}{5}$ rounds to 0.

1 is much smaller than 5.

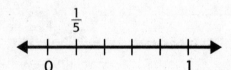

Round each number to 0, $\frac{1}{2}$, or 1.

1. $\frac{9}{10}$ _____   2. $\frac{1}{10}$ _____   3. $\frac{5}{8}$ _____

4. $\frac{2}{7}$ _____   5. $\frac{9}{16}$ _____   6. $\frac{1}{3}$ _____

7. $\frac{2}{3}$ _____   8. $\frac{6}{7}$ _____   9. $\frac{4}{9}$ _____

10. $\frac{5}{11}$ _____   11. $\frac{1}{8}$ _____   12. $\frac{7}{8}$ _____

Skills Practice

Round Fractions

Round each number to 0, $\frac{1}{2}$ or 1.

1. $\frac{1}{12}$ _____

2. $\frac{12}{13}$ _____

3. $\frac{9}{18}$ _____

4. $\frac{3}{4}$ _____

5. $\frac{2}{9}$ _____

6. $\frac{2}{3}$ _____

7. $\frac{1}{2}$ _____

8. $\frac{3}{8}$ _____

9. $\frac{7}{8}$ _____

10. $\frac{1}{8}$ _____

11. $\frac{12}{15}$ _____

12. $\frac{2}{9}$ _____

13. $\frac{1}{4}$ _____

14. $\frac{11}{12}$ _____

15. $\frac{5}{6}$ _____

16. $\frac{2}{16}$ _____

17. $\frac{1}{3}$ _____

18. $\frac{4}{5}$ _____

19. $\frac{1}{8}$ _____

20. $\frac{1}{5}$ _____

21. $\frac{8}{9}$ _____

Solve.

22. Mrs. Jones is putting up blinds to fit in a window opening that is $\frac{7}{8}$ yard wide. Should she round $\frac{7}{8}$ up or down when deciding on the size of blinds to purchase?

_____

23. Marvin is mailing a copy of a document that is $12\frac{1}{8}$ inches long and $10\frac{1}{2}$ inches wide. Will the document fit in an envelope that is 12 inches long and $10\frac{1}{2}$ inches wide or in an envelope that is $12\frac{1}{2}$ inches long and 11 inches wide?

_____

Name _____ Date _____

Homework Practice

Round Fractions

Round each number to 0, $\frac{1}{2}$, or 1.

1. $\frac{1}{12}$ _____

2. $\frac{5}{11}$ _____

3. $\frac{3}{10}$ _____

4. $\frac{8}{12}$ _____

5. $\frac{2}{9}$ _____

6. $\frac{14}{16}$ _____

7. $\frac{6}{16}$ _____

8. $\frac{7}{12}$ _____

9. $\frac{3}{8}$ _____

Solve.

10. Your basement has an $8\frac{3}{12}$ foot ceiling. To the nearest half foot, how tall is the tallest cabinet that can fit in the basement?

_____

11. Alice is giving a book as a gift that is $8\frac{3}{8}$ inches long and $6\frac{1}{12}$ inches wide. Will the book fit in a box that is $8\frac{1}{2}$ inches long and $6\frac{1}{2}$ inches wide or in a box that is 8 inches long and 6 inches wide?

_____

Spiral Review

Replace $\bigcirc$ with < or > to make a true statement. (Lesson 8-5).

12. $\frac{3}{4} \bigcirc \frac{1}{4}$

13. $\frac{4}{7} \bigcirc \frac{5}{7}$

14. $2\frac{1}{9} \bigcirc 1\frac{2}{9}$

15. $1\frac{2}{3} \bigcirc 2\frac{1}{3}$

16. $\frac{9}{6} \bigcirc \frac{5}{6}$

17. $3\frac{1}{12} \bigcirc 2\frac{11}{12}$

Name _____ Date _____

Problem-Solving Practice

Round Fractions

Solve.

1. A recipe for cookies calls for $\frac{3}{4}$ of a cup of chocolate chips. Should you buy a package with $\frac{1}{2}$ cup or a package with 1 cup?

   _____

2. The cookie recipe also calls for $\frac{3}{8}$ of a cup of walnuts. Should you buy a package with 1 cup or a package with $\frac{1}{2}$ cup of walnuts?

   _____

3. Your kitchen has a $9\frac{3}{4}$ foot ceiling. To the nearest half foot, what is the tallest refrigerator that can fit in the kitchen under a cabinet that hangs down 3 feet?

   _____

4. Russ is putting his photographs in an album that is $12\frac{1}{8}$ inches long and $10\frac{1}{2}$ inches wide. Should he trim the edges of the photographs to 12 inches long and 10 inches wide or to $12\frac{1}{2}$ inches long and $10\frac{1}{2}$ inches wide?

   _____

5. A farmer is planting squash plants that need $2\frac{3}{8}$ feet to spread out. He has an area along a fence that is 20 feet long. Round the amount of space the squash plants need to the nearest $\frac{1}{2}$ foot. How many squash plants can the farmer grow along the fence?

   _____

6. Based on the area of his flowerbed, a gardener calculates that he needs $6\frac{8}{14}$ gallons of fertilizer. Should he round $6\frac{8}{14}$ up or down when deciding on the amount of fertilizer he should purchase?

   _____

Name _____ Date _____

Enrich

Greatest Possible Error

When you measure a quantity, your measurement is more precise when you use a smaller unit of measure. But no measurement is ever exact—there is always some amount of error. The greatest possible error (GPE) of a measurement is one half the unit of measure.

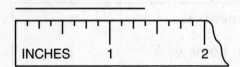

unit of measure: $\frac{1}{8}$ inch

length of line segment: $1\frac{3}{8}$ inches

GPE: half of $\frac{1}{8}$ inch, or $\frac{1}{16}$ inch

Since $1\frac{3}{8} = 1\frac{6}{16}$, the actual measure of the line segment may range anywhere from $1\frac{5}{16}$ inches to $1\frac{7}{16}$ inches.

Use the GPE to give a range for the measure of each line segment.

1. _____

2. _____

3. _____

4. _____

5. Using this scale, the weight of a bag of potatoes is measured as 3 pounds. What is the range for the actual weight of the potatoes?

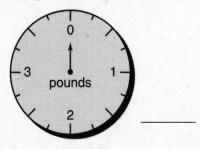

_____

6. Using this container, the amount of a liquid is measured as 20 milliliters. What is the range for the actual amount of the liquid?

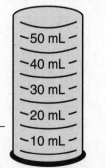

_____

Name _____ Date _____

Reteach

Problem-Solving Investigation: Choose the Best Strategy

Fina did a survey of how much time students spend on homework each night. Out of 16 people interviewed, $\frac{1}{2}$ spend about 1 hour on homework and $\frac{1}{4}$ spend about 45 minutes on homework. The rest spend about 30 minutes on homework. How many students spend 30 minutes on homework?

Understand	$\frac{1}{2}$ of 16 students spend 1 hour on homework. $\frac{1}{4}$ of 16 students spend 45 minutes on homework. You need to know how many people spend 30 minutes on homework.
Plan	You can use the *act it out* strategy. Draw 16 students. Cross out the students who spend 1 hour and the students who spend 45 minutes on homework. You will be left with the students who spend 30 minutes on homework.
Solve	$\frac{1}{2}$ of 16 is 8. Cross out 8 students. ☺ ☺ ☺ ☺ ☺ ☺ ☺ ☺ ☺ ☺ ☺ ☺ ☺ ☺ ☺ ☺ $\frac{1}{4}$ of 16 is 4. Cross out 4 more students. Count the students that are left. 4 students spend about 30 minutes on homework.
Check	Use math to check your work. $16 - 8 - 4 = 4$ Your answer is correct.

Name _____ Date _____

Reteach

Problem-Solving Investigation (continued)

Use any strategy shown below to solve.

- Act it out
- Make a table
- Use logical reasoning
- Guess and check
- Work backward
- Solve a simpler problem

1. Out of the 200 students at Groves High, 50 spend 2 hours a night on homework, 25 spend 1 hour on homework, and 75 spend 45 minutes on homework. The rest spend 30 minutes on homework. How many students spend 30 minutes on homework?

_____

2. Mrs. Jones told her class of 30 students that 8 people scored 90 or above on a math test, 7 people scored between 80 and 89 and 10 people scored between 70 and 79. How many people scored lower than 70?

_____

3. If square tables are arranged in a restaurant so that only one person can sit on any side of the table, how many tables will it take to seat 40 people?

_____

4. Alan bought a computer that was on sale for $568. If the computer originally cost $647, how much money did Alan save?

_____

5. Forty people in a restaurant spend a total of $500. $\frac{1}{2}$ of the 40 people spend $20 each. What is the least amount of money each of the rest of the people spend?

_____

Name _____ Date _____

Skills Practice

Problem-Solving Investigation: Choose the Best Strategy

Use any strategy shown below to solve.

- Guess and check
- Make a table
- Work backward
- Use logical reasoning
- Solve a simpler problem
- Act it out

1. In how many ways can 5 people stand in line if one of the people always has to be first in line?

_____

2. The teacher told the class of 30 students that $\frac{1}{2}$ of them scored above an 80 on their math test. An additional $\frac{1}{3}$ of them scored at least a 70. How many of them scored below 70?

_____

3. Alicia bought a CD player for $10 less than the regular price. If she paid $58 for the CD player, what was the regular price?

_____

4. Miguel bought boxes of chocolates. The first box weighed $4\frac{1}{4}$ pounds, the second, $2\frac{3}{4}$, and the third, $1\frac{1}{3}$. What is the total amount of chocolate that Miguel bought?

_____

5. After Miguel shared the chocolate with his friends, he had $3\frac{5}{8}$ pounds left. Then, he gave $2\frac{3}{4}$ pounds to his mother. Now, how much does he have?

_____

6. The first $\frac{1}{5}$ mile of a $\frac{3}{4}$-mile path through a rose garden is paved with bricks. How much of the path is not paved with bricks?

_____

Name _____ Date _____

Homework Practice

Problem-Solving Investigation: Choose the Best Strategy

Use any strategy shown below to solve.

- Guess and check
- Work backward
- Solve a simpler problem
- Make a table
- Use logical reasoning
- Act it out

1. Olivia bought a ring for $\frac{1}{2}$ off the regular price. If she paid $50, what was the regular price?

_____

2. Mrs. Jones told the class that $\frac{1}{3}$ of them scored 90 or above on the math test. Another $\frac{1}{3}$ of them had a passing score. What fraction of the class failed?

_____

3. At a park, a picnic shelter covers $\frac{1}{4}$ of an acre and a playground covers $\frac{5}{8}$ of an acre. How much area is covered by both the picnic shelter and the playground?

_____

4. Of the 300 students at school, 110 are in the chorus and 150 are in the band. Of these students, 50 are in both chorus and the band. How many students are neither in the chorus nor the band?

_____

Spiral Review

Round each fraction to 0, $\frac{1}{2}$, or 1.

5. $\frac{1}{7}$ _____

6. $\frac{7}{8}$ _____

7. $\frac{2}{10}$ _____

8. $\frac{5}{6}$ _____

9. $\frac{5}{9}$ _____

10. $\frac{4}{10}$ _____

Enrich

Choose the Operation

Solve.

1. A box is $\frac{1}{2}$ inch tall. If 5 of the boxes are stacked on top of each other, how tall is the stack of boxes?

   _____

2. Darlene needs $\frac{3}{4}$ yard of fabric to cover a chair. She has $\frac{3}{8}$ yard of fabric. How much more fabric does she need?

   _____

3. Mr. Montgomery is a chef. He has created 250 new recipes. He plans to donate $\frac{3}{5}$ of them to the school library. How many recipes does he plan to donate?

   _____

4. The art department received a shipment of 6 boxes of clay. Each box weighed $\frac{3}{4}$ pound. How many pounds of clay were in the shipment?

   _____

5. A sculptor has a steel tube that is $\frac{2}{3}$ foot long. To create a longer tube, he attaches it to another steel tube that is $\frac{5}{6}$ foot long. How long is the new steel tube?

   _____

6. Marcel was in a triathalon, a race with 3 events. He ran 4 miles in $\frac{2}{3}$ hour. He bicycled 5 miles in $\frac{3}{4}$ hour, and he swam 880 yards in $\frac{1}{2}$ hour. What was his total race time?

   _____

Name _____ Date _____

Individual Progress Checklist

Learning Mastery			Lesson	Lesson Goal	Comments
B	D	M			
			8-1	Represent division situations using fractions.	
			8-2	Write improper fractions as mixed numbers.	
			8-3	Solve problems by using logical reasoning.	
			8-4	Write mixed numbers as improper fractions.	
			8-5	Compare fractions and mixed numbers using a number line.	
			8-6	Round fractions to 0, $\frac{1}{2}$, 1 using a number line.	
			8-7	Choose the best strategy to solve a problem.	

B = Beginning; **D** = Developing; **M** = Mastered

Note to Parents

_____

_____

_____

_____

_____

_____

_____

_____

Assessment

Name _____ Date _____

Chapter Diagnostic Test

Write the fraction that names the shaded part of the whole or set.

1.

2.

3.

1. _____

2. _____

3. _____

Divide.

4. 15 ÷ 3

5. 33 ÷ 6

6. 40 ÷ 8

7. 23 ÷ 7

4. _____

5. _____

6. _____

7. _____

Use the number line below for Exercises 8–10. Replace each ____ with < or > to make a true statement.

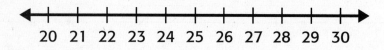

8. 25 ____ 26

9. 27 ____ 24

10. 30 ____ 20

8. _____

9. _____

10. _____

Name _____ Date _____

Chapter Pretest

Represent each situation using a fraction. Then solve.

1. George, Paul, and Courtney are sharing 2 grapefruits. How much does each person get?

2. In science class, there are 3 gallons of water for 5 groups. How much water will each group receive?

Write each improper fraction as a mixed number.

3. $\frac{5}{3}$ _____   4. $\frac{7}{4}$ _____   5. $\frac{30}{7}$ _____

Write each mixed number as an improper fraction.

6. $1\frac{4}{5}$ _____   7. $4\frac{3}{4}$ _____   8. $3\frac{4}{7}$ _____

Use the number line for Exercises 9–10. Replace each  **with < or > to make a true statement.**

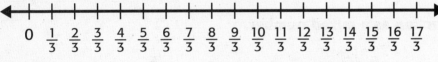

9. $\frac{5}{3}$ ◯ $\frac{2}{3}$ 10. $2\frac{2}{3}$ ◯ $\frac{16}{3}$

Round each fraction to 0, $\frac{1}{2}$, or 1.

11. $\frac{8}{9}$ _____   12. $\frac{4}{10}$ _____   13. $\frac{1}{6}$ _____

Solve.

14. For science class, Mr. Hernandez must divide 8 pounds of sand into 12 equal containers. How much sand will he put in each container?

15. What two positive integers have a sum of 12 and a product of 35?

1. _____

2. _____

3. _____

4. _____

5. _____

6. _____

7. _____

8. _____

9. _____

10. _____

11. _____

12. _____

13. _____

14. _____

15. _____

Name _____ Date _____

Quiz 1 *(Lessons 8–1 through 8–2)*

Represent each situation using a fraction. Then solve.

1. Five people will equally share two pizzas. How much pizza will each person receive?

   1. _____

2. Mr. Johansen is cutting construction paper for an art project. He has 24 students, and 6 large pieces of construction paper. How much paper will each student receive?

   2. _____

3. Greg is pouring an entire gallon of milk into 10 glasses. What part of a gallon will be in each glass?

   3. _____

4. Sara is cutting ribbon for a craft project. She has 4 feet of ribbon, which must be cut into 7 equal lengths. How long will each piece of ribbon be after she has finished cutting?

   4. _____

Write each improper fraction as a mixed number.

5. $\frac{3}{2}$ 6. $\frac{12}{5}$

   5. _____

7. $\frac{48}{13}$ 8. $\frac{17}{4}$

   6. _____

9. $\frac{20}{11}$ 10. $\frac{9}{2}$

   7. _____

   8. _____

   9. _____

   10. _____

Name _____ Date _____

Quiz 2 *(Lessons 8–3 through 8–4)*

Solve.

1. Six students are playing basketball. One student arrives, and at the same time, 2 students leave. Then, 1 more student leaves and 3 more arrive. Now how many students are playing basketball?

2. John has 3 quarters, 5 dimes, 2 nickels, and 5 pennies. How many different combinations of coins can he make to have $0.60?

3. Ann is using a roll of shelf paper to line 10 shelves that are all the same size. The roll of paper has $25\frac{1}{2}$ feet on it. She has already used $4\frac{1}{3}$ feet on 1 shelf. Will she have enough to line the other 9 shelves?

4. Sandra and Janice are painting flowers in a border around two walls of a room. They each are doing one wall. Sandra has $\frac{1}{3}$ of her wall painted in 2 hours. How much longer will it take Sandra to finish her wall?

1. _____

2. _____

3. _____

4. _____

Write each mixed number as an improper fraction.

5. $3\frac{3}{4}$

6. $2\frac{5}{8}$

7. $1\frac{1}{12}$

8. $7\frac{9}{12}$

9. $2\frac{3}{4}$

10. $5\frac{6}{7}$

5. _____

6. _____

7. _____

8. _____

9. _____

10. _____

Name _____ Date _____

Quiz 3 *(Lessons 8–5 through 8–7)*

Use the number line for Exercises 1–4. Replace each ◯
with < or > to make a true statement.

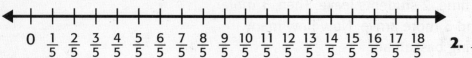

$$0 \quad \frac{1}{5} \quad \frac{2}{5} \quad \frac{3}{5} \quad \frac{4}{5} \quad \frac{5}{5} \quad \frac{6}{5} \quad \frac{7}{5} \quad \frac{8}{5} \quad \frac{9}{5} \quad \frac{10}{5} \quad \frac{11}{5} \quad \frac{12}{5} \quad \frac{13}{5} \quad \frac{14}{5} \quad \frac{15}{5} \quad \frac{16}{5} \quad \frac{17}{5} \quad \frac{18}{5}$$

1. $\frac{4}{5}$ ◯ $\frac{7}{5}$ **2.** $\frac{14}{5}$ ◯ $\frac{11}{5}$

3. $\frac{3}{5}$ ◯ $\frac{12}{5}$ **4.** $\frac{10}{5}$ ◯ $\frac{14}{5}$

Round each fraction to 0, $\frac{1}{2}$, or 1.

5. $\frac{1}{10}$ **6.** $\frac{8}{9}$

7. $\frac{4}{11}$ **8.** $\frac{12}{15}$

Solve.

9. How many ways can you make change for a $20-bill using only $5 and $10 bills?

10. Marcia is practicing for the track team. On Monday, she ran for 10 minutes. Each day for the rest of the week, she ran for 3 minutes longer than the previous day. How many minutes did she run on Thursday?

1. _____

2. _____

3. _____

4. _____

5. _____

6. _____

7. _____

8. _____

9. _____

10. _____

Name _____ Date _____

Mid-Chapter Test *(Lessons 8–1 through 8–4)*

Read each question carefully. Write your answer on the line provided.

1. One large salad is divided among 4 people. How much of the salad does each person receive?

    A. $\frac{1}{4}$ C. $\frac{1}{2}$

    B. $\frac{1}{3}$ D. 1

2. What is $\frac{10}{7}$ written as a mixed number?

    F. $1\frac{1}{10}$ H. $1\frac{3}{7}$

    G. $1\frac{1}{7}$ J. $2\frac{1}{7}$

3. What is $\frac{11}{5}$ written as a mixed number?

    A. $1\frac{1}{5}$ C. $3\frac{2}{5}$

    B. $2\frac{1}{5}$ D. $3\frac{3}{5}$

4. What is $8\frac{1}{2}$ written as an improper fraction?

    F. $\frac{4}{12}$ H. $\frac{11}{2}$

    G. $\frac{7}{2}$ J. $\frac{17}{2}$

5. What is $1\frac{4}{5}$ written as an improper fraction?

    A. $\frac{9}{5}$ C. $\frac{15}{5}$

    B. $\frac{11}{5}$ D. $\frac{18}{5}$

6. How do you change an improper fraction to a mixed number? _____

7. How do you change a mixed number to an improper fraction? _____

8. How can you tell if a fraction can be written as a mixed number? _____

9. What is $\frac{9}{4}$ written as a mixed number? _____

10. What is $3\frac{2}{7}$ written as an improper fraction? _____

1. _____

2. _____

3. _____

4. _____

5. _____

6. _____

7. _____

8. _____

9. _____

10. _____

Vocabulary Test

Using the word bank below, complete each sentence by writing the correct word or words on the line provided.

improper fraction	numerator	denominator
fraction	mixed number	

1. The _____ is the number above the bar in a fraction; the part of the fraction that tells how many of the equal parts are being used.

   1. _____

2. A _____ has a whole number part and a fraction part.

   2. _____

3. An _____ is a fraction that has a numerator that is greater than or equal to its denominator.

   3. _____

4. The bottom number in a fraction is the _____.

   4. _____

5. A number that represents part of a whole or part of a set is a _____.

   5. _____

Oral Assessment

Draw 2 squares on the board. Divide each square into 4 equal parts. For the first square, shade in all sections. For the second square, shade in 1 section.

Read each question aloud to the student. Then write the student's answers on the lines below the question.

1. How many parts are shaded in the first square?

_____

2. How many parts are shaded in the second square?

_____

3. What is the fraction that represents the amount of parts shaded on the second square?

_____

4. Tell how you got your answer.

_____

_____

5. How would you write the total number of shaded squares as an improper fraction?

_____

6. Tell how you got your answer.

_____

_____

7. How do you change this improper fraction to a mixed number?

_____

_____

8. What is this improper fraction as a mixed number?

_____

Draw 2 circles on the board. Divide each circle into 3 equal parts. For the first circle, shade in 2 sections. For the second circle, shade in 1 section.

9. How can you write the shaded portion of the first circle as a fraction?

_____

10. How can you write the shaded portion of the second circle as a fraction?

_____

11. Which fraction is larger?

_____

8

Chapter Project Rubric

Score	Explanation
3	Student successfully completed the chapter project.
	Student demonstrated appropriate use of chapter information in completing the chapter project.
2	Student completed the chapter project with partial success.
	Student partially demonstrated appropriate use of chapter information in completing the chapter project.
1	Student completed the chapter project with little success.
	Student demonstrated very little appropriate use of chapter information in completing the chapter project.
0	Student did not complete the chapter project.
	Student demonstrated inappropriate use of chapter information in completing the chapter project.

Assessment

Name _____ Date _____

Chapter Foldables® Rubric

Fractions

Layered Look Foldable

Score	Explanation
3	Student properly assembled Foldables® graphic organizer according to instructions. Student recorded information related to the chapter in the manner directed by the Foldables graphic organizer. Student used the Foldables graphic organizer as a study guide and organizational tool.
2	Student exhibited partial understanding of proper Foldables graphic organizer assembly. Student recorded most but not all information related to the chapter in the manner directed by the Foldables graphic organizer. Student demonstrated partial use of the Foldables graphic organizer as a study guide and organizational tool.
1	Student showed little understanding of proper Foldables graphic organizer assembly. Student recorded only some information related to the chapter in the manner directed by the Foldables graphic organizer. Student demonstrated little use of the Foldables graphic organizer as a study guide and organizational tool.
0	Student did not assemble Foldables graphic organizer according to instructions. Student recorded little or no information related to the chapter in the manner directed by the Foldables graphic organizer. Student did not use the Foldables graphic organizer as a study guide and organizational tool.

Name _____ Date _____

Chapter Test, Form 1

Read each question carefully. Write your answer on the line provided.

Represent each situation using a fraction. Then solve.

1. John is making 7 banners. He has 4 yards of fabric. How many yards of fabric will he use to make each banner?

   A. $\frac{1}{7}$ yard **B.** $\frac{3}{7}$ yard **C.** $\frac{4}{7}$ yard **D.** $\frac{6}{7}$ yard

   1. _____

2. Mr. Martinez has a box containing 11 granola bars. After handing out 3 granola bars, what fraction of the whole box does Mr. Martinez have left?

   F. $\frac{1}{11}$ **G.** $\frac{3}{11}$ **H.** $\frac{5}{11}$ **J.** $\frac{8}{11}$

   2. _____

Choose the equivalent mixed number for each improper fraction.

3. $\frac{4}{3}$

   A. $1\frac{1}{3}$ **B.** $1\frac{2}{3}$ **C.** $2\frac{1}{3}$ **D.** $2\frac{2}{3}$

   3. _____

4. $\frac{14}{9}$

   F. $1\frac{1}{9}$ **G.** $1\frac{5}{9}$ **H.** $1\frac{7}{9}$ **J.** $2\frac{1}{9}$

   4. _____

5. $\frac{23}{5}$

   A. $2\frac{3}{5}$ **B.** $2\frac{4}{5}$ **C.** $4\frac{1}{5}$ **D.** $4\frac{3}{5}$

   5. _____

Choose the equivalent improper fraction for each mixed number.

6. $5\frac{1}{4}$

   F. $\frac{25}{4}$ **G.** $\frac{23}{4}$ **H.** $\frac{21}{4}$ **J.** $\frac{17}{4}$

   6. _____

7. $3\frac{6}{7}$

   A. $\frac{32}{7}$ **B.** $\frac{27}{7}$ **C.** $\frac{18}{7}$ **D.** $\frac{13}{7}$

   7. _____

8. $5\frac{2}{3}$

   F. $\frac{17}{3}$ **G.** $\frac{19}{3}$ **H.** $\frac{24}{3}$ **J.** $\frac{25}{3}$

   8. _____

Use the number line for questions 9–12.

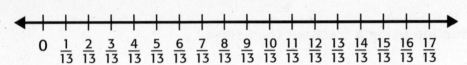

$$0 \quad \frac{1}{13} \quad \frac{2}{13} \quad \frac{3}{13} \quad \frac{4}{13} \quad \frac{5}{13} \quad \frac{6}{13} \quad \frac{7}{13} \quad \frac{8}{13} \quad \frac{9}{13} \quad \frac{10}{13} \quad \frac{11}{13} \quad \frac{12}{13} \quad \frac{13}{13} \quad \frac{14}{13} \quad \frac{15}{13} \quad \frac{16}{13} \quad \frac{17}{13}$$

9. $\frac{8}{13} \bigcirc \frac{6}{13}$

   A. <　　　　**B.** >　　　　**C.** =

10. $\frac{3}{13} \bigcirc \frac{7}{13}$

   F. <　　　　**G.** >　　　　**H.** =

11. $\frac{9}{13} \bigcirc \frac{2}{13}$

   A. <　　　　**B.** >　　　　**C.** =

12. $1\frac{1}{3} \bigcirc \frac{4}{3}$

   F. <　　　　**G.** >　　　　**H.** =

Round each fraction to 0, $\frac{1}{2}$, or 1.

13. $\frac{1}{7}$

   A. 0　　　　**B.** $\frac{1}{2}$　　　　**C.** 1

14. $\frac{4}{9}$

   F. 0　　　　**G.** $\frac{1}{2}$　　　　**H.** 1

Solve.

15. Janice has 7 more apples than pears. She has 9 apples and pears in all. How many pears does she have?

   A. 2 pears　　　**B.** 4 pears　　　**C.** 6 pears　　　**D.** 8 pears

16. What two numbers have a sum of 14 and a product of 48?

   F. 5 and 9　　　**G.** 3 and 9　　　**H.** 4 and 8　　　**J.** 6 and 8

9. _____

10. _____

11. _____

12. _____

13. _____

14. _____

15. _____

16. _____

Name _____ Date _____

Chapter Test, Form 2A

Read each question carefully. Write your answer on the line provided.

Write each improper fraction as an equivalent mixed number.

1. $\frac{5}{3}$

   A. $1\frac{1}{3}$ **B.** $1\frac{2}{3}$ **C.** $2\frac{1}{3}$ **D.** $2\frac{2}{3}$

   1. _____

2. $\frac{11}{9}$

   F. $1\frac{2}{9}$ **G.** $1\frac{5}{9}$ **H.** $1\frac{7}{9}$ **J.** $2\frac{2}{9}$

   2. _____

3. $\frac{18}{5}$

   A. $2\frac{3}{5}$ **B.** $2\frac{4}{5}$ **C.** $3\frac{3}{5}$ **D.** $4\frac{3}{5}$

   3. _____

Represent each situation using a fraction or mixed number. Then solve.

4. Catherine is making 4 costumes. She has 10 yards of fabric. How many yards of fabric will she use to make each costume?

   F. $\frac{4}{10}$ yard   **G.** $2\frac{1}{4}$ yards   **H.** $2\frac{2}{5}$ yards   **J.** $2\frac{1}{2}$ yards

   4. _____

5. Chelsea has a box containing 12 markers. After handing out 7 markers, what fraction of the markers does Chelsea have left?

   A. $\frac{1}{12}$ **B.** $\frac{3}{12}$ **C.** $\frac{5}{12}$ **D.** $\frac{8}{12}$

   5. _____

Write each mixed number as an equivalent improper fraction.

6. $3\frac{1}{2}$

   F. $\frac{7}{2}$ **G.** $\frac{8}{2}$ **H.** $\frac{9}{2}$ **J.** $\frac{9}{3}$

   6. _____

7. $3\frac{2}{7}$

   A. $\frac{32}{7}$ **B.** $\frac{23}{7}$ **C.** $\frac{17}{7}$ **D.** $\frac{15}{7}$

   7. _____

8. $10\frac{5}{6}$

   F. $\frac{80}{6}$ **G.** $\frac{75}{6}$ **H.** $\frac{65}{6}$ **J.** $\frac{60}{6}$

   8. _____

Name _____ Date _____

Use the number line for questions 9–12.

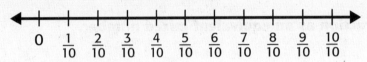

9. Which number is greater than $\frac{5}{10}$?

   A. $\frac{3}{10}$ **B.** $\frac{4}{10}$ **C.** $\frac{5}{10}$ **D.** $\frac{6}{10}$ 9. _____

10. Which number is less than $\frac{3}{10}$?

   F. 0   **G.** $\frac{3}{10}$ **H.** $\frac{4}{10}$ **J.** $\frac{7}{10}$ 10. _____

11. Which number is greater than $\frac{10}{20}$?

   A. $\frac{3}{10}$ **B.** $\frac{4}{10}$ **C.** $\frac{5}{10}$ **D.** $\frac{6}{10}$ 11. _____

12. Which number is equal to $\frac{4}{5}$?

   F. $\frac{7}{10}$ **G.** $\frac{8}{10}$ **H.** $\frac{9}{10}$ **J.** 1   12. _____

Write the fraction or mixed number that is represented by each point.

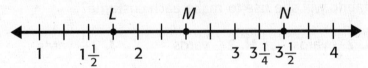

13. *L*

   A. $1\frac{1}{2}$ **B.** $1\frac{3}{4}$ **C.** $2\frac{1}{4}$ **D.** $2\frac{3}{4}$ 13. _____

14. *M*

   F. $2\frac{1}{4}$ **G.** $2\frac{1}{2}$ **H.** $2\frac{3}{4}$ **G.** $2\frac{4}{5}$ 14. _____

Solve.

15. Neil has 5 more apples than pears. He has 9 apples and pears in all.
    How many pears does he have?

   A. 2 pears   **B.** 3 pears   **C.** 4 pears   **D.** 8 pears   15. _____

16. What two numbers have a sum of 12 and a product of 35?

   F. 5 and 9   **G.** 5 and 8   **H.** 6 and 7   **J.** 5 and 7   16 _____

Name _____ Date _____

Chapter Test, Form 2B

Assessment

Read each question carefully. Write your answer on the line provided.

Use the number line for questions 1–4.

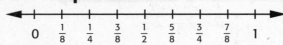

1. Which number is greater than $\frac{5}{8}$?

    A. $\frac{3}{8}$ **B.** $\frac{2}{8}$ **C.** $\frac{5}{8}$ **D.** $\frac{3}{4}$

    1. _____

2. Which number is less than $\frac{1}{4}$?

    F. $\frac{1}{8}$ **G.** $\frac{2}{8}$ **H.** $\frac{1}{2}$ **J.** $\frac{7}{8}$

    2. _____

3. Which number is greater than $\frac{5}{10}$?

    A. $\frac{6}{8}$ **B.** $\frac{4}{8}$ **C.** $\frac{2}{8}$ **D.** $\frac{1}{8}$

    3. _____

4. Which number is equal to 1?

    F. $\frac{8}{8}$ **G.** $\frac{7}{8}$ **H.** $\frac{5}{8}$ **J.** 0

    4. _____

Write each improper fraction as an equivalent mixed number.

5. $\frac{33}{8}$

    A. $4\frac{7}{8}$ **B.** $4\frac{1}{8}$ **C.** $3\frac{7}{8}$ **D.** $3\frac{1}{8}$

    5. _____

6. $\frac{13}{2}$

    F. $5\frac{1}{2}$ **G.** $5\frac{2}{3}$ **H.** $6\frac{1}{2}$ **J.** $7\frac{1}{2}$

    6. _____

7. $\frac{21}{5}$

    A. $3\frac{3}{4}$ **B.** $4\frac{1}{5}$ **C.** $4\frac{2}{5}$ **D.** $5\frac{1}{5}$

    7. _____

Solve.

8. Frasier is making 4 pillowcases. He has 2 yards of fabric. How many yards of fabric will he use to make each pillowcase?

    F. $\frac{4}{2}$ yards   **G.** $\frac{3}{4}$ yard   **H.** $\frac{1}{2}$ yard   **J.** $\frac{1}{4}$ yard

    8. _____

9. Sue has a box containing 24 crayons. After handing out 8 crayons, what fraction of the box does she have left?

    A. $\frac{8}{24}$ **B.** $\frac{1}{3}$ **C.** $\frac{1}{2}$ **D.** $\frac{2}{3}$

    9. _____

Write the fraction or mixed number that names each point.

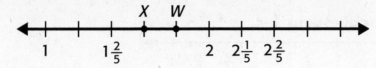

10. *X*

    F. $1\frac{2}{5}$ **G.** $1\frac{3}{5}$ **H.** $1\frac{4}{5}$ **J.** 2   10. _____

11. *W*

    A. $1\frac{4}{5}$ **B.** $2\frac{1}{5}$ **C.** $2\frac{2}{5}$ **D.** $2\frac{3}{5}$ 11. _____

Write each mixed number as an equivalent improper fraction.

12. $10\frac{3}{4}$

    F. $\frac{33}{4}$ **G.** $\frac{34}{4}$ **H.** $\frac{40}{4}$ **J.** $\frac{43}{4}$ 12. _____

13. $3\frac{2}{3}$

    A. $\frac{11}{9}$ **B.** $\frac{11}{3}$ **C.** $\frac{11}{9}$ **D.** $\frac{9}{2}$ 13. _____

14. $21\frac{2}{3}$

    F. $\frac{70}{3}$ **G.** $\frac{65}{3}$ **H.** $\frac{65}{6}$ **J.** $\frac{63}{3}$ 14. _____

Solve.

15. Art class starts at 6:00 P.M. and lasts 1 hour and 15 minutes. At what time does the class end?

    A. 6:30 P.M.   **B.** 7:00 P.M.   **C.** 7:05 P.M.   **D.** 7:15 P.M.   15. _____

16. What two numbers have a sum of 16 and a product of 63?

    F. 5 and 9   **G.** 5 and 8   **H.** 6 and 9   **J.** 7 and 9   16. _____

Name _____ Date _____

Chapter Test, Form 2C

Read each question carefully. Fill in the correct answer on the line provided.

Write the fraction or mixed number that is represented by each point.

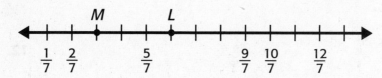

$\frac{1}{7}$ $\frac{2}{7}$ $\frac{5}{7}$ $\frac{9}{7}$ $\frac{10}{7}$ $\frac{12}{7}$

1. _____

2. _____

1. L

2. M

Solve.

3. _____

3. A piece of ribbon needs to be cut into 9 pieces. How many cuts will have to be made?

4. _____

4. What two numbers have a product of 72 and a sum of 17?

Write each improper fraction as an equivalent mixed number.

5. _____

5. $\frac{8}{3}$

6. _____

6. $\frac{53}{10}$

7. $\frac{69}{5}$

7. _____

Represent each situation using a fraction or mixed number. Then solve.

8. _____

8. Rudy is making 3 tablecloths. He has 10 yards of fabric. How many yards of fabric will he use to make each tablecloth?

9. _____

9. Roxanne has a box containing 48 beads. After giving away 16 beads, what fraction of the beads does Roxanne have left?

Write each mixed number as an equivalent improper fraction.

10. $5\frac{7}{8}$

11. $3\frac{2}{3}$

12. $13\frac{9}{10}$

10. _____

11. _____

12. _____

Use the number line for questions 13–16. Replace each ◯ with < or > to make a true statement.

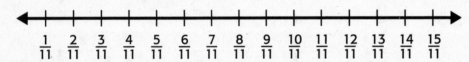

13. $\frac{3}{11}$ ◯ $\frac{5}{11}$

14. $\frac{8}{11}$ ◯ $\frac{7}{11}$

15. $\frac{13}{11}$ ◯ $\frac{15}{11}$

16. $\frac{11}{11}$ ◯ $\frac{10}{11}$

13. _____

14. _____

15. _____

16. _____

Name _____ Date _____

Chapter Test, Form 2D

Read each question carefully. Fill in the correct answer on the line provided.

Solve.

1. A piece of ribbon needs to be cut into 13 pieces. How many cuts will have to be made?

1. _____

2. What two positive numbers have a product of 20 and a sum of 9?

2. _____

Write each as an equivalent mixed number.

3. $\frac{14}{4}$

3. _____

4. $\frac{37}{8}$

4. _____

5. $\frac{75}{2}$

5. _____

Write the fraction or mixed number at each point.

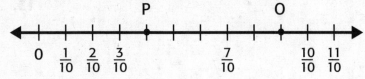

6. O

6. _____

7. P

7. _____

Represent each situation using a fraction or mixed number. Then solve.

8. Charlotte is making 5 scarves. She has 7 balls of yarn. How many balls of yarn will she use on each scarf?

8. _____

9. Esther has 32 muffins. After giving away 16 muffins, what fraction of the muffins does she have left?

9. _____

Write each mixed number as an equivalent improper fraction.

10. $7\dfrac{3}{5}$

10. _____

11. $4\dfrac{9}{13}$

11. _____

12. $8\dfrac{5}{6}$

12. _____

Use the number line for questions 13–16. Replace each ◯ with < or > to make a true statement.

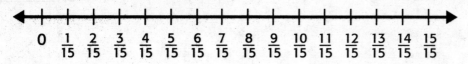

13. $\dfrac{7}{15}$ ◯ $\dfrac{5}{15}$

13. _____

14. $\dfrac{8}{15}$ ◯ $\dfrac{10}{15}$

14. _____

15. $\dfrac{13}{15}$ ◯ $\dfrac{15}{15}$

15. _____

16. $\dfrac{1}{15}$ ◯ $\dfrac{2}{15}$

16. _____

Name _____ Date _____

Chapter Test, Form 3

Write each improper fraction as an equivalent mixed number.

1. $\dfrac{94}{3}$

2. $\dfrac{282}{8}$

3. $\dfrac{69}{14}$

1. _____

2. _____

3. _____

Represent each situation using a fraction or mixed number. Then solve.

4. Tamara is making 5 pillowcases. She needs $\dfrac{3}{5}$ yard of fabric for each pillowcase. She has $2\dfrac{4}{5}$ yards of fabric. Does she have enough fabric?

5. Marcus has a box containing 46 pencils. After giving away 36 pencils, what fraction of the pencils does he have left?

4. _____

5. _____

Write the fraction or mixed number in simplest form that is represented by each point.

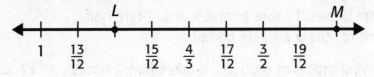

6. L

7. M

6. _____

7. _____

Use the number line for questions 8–9. Replace each ◯ with < or > to make a true statement.

8. $\dfrac{8}{11}$ ◯ $\dfrac{5}{11}$

9. $\dfrac{10}{11}$ ◯ $\dfrac{7}{11}$

8. _____

9. _____

Write each mixed number as an equivalent improper fraction.

10. $7\frac{3}{5}$

10. _____

11. $2\frac{33}{35}$

11. _____

12. $4\frac{28}{67}$

12. _____

Solve.

13. A piece of rope needs to be cut into 10 pieces. How many cuts will have to be made?

13. _____

14. What two numbers have a sum of 19 and a product of 90?

14. _____

15. Francis makes two square pans of cornbread. He cuts one pan into 13 more pieces than the other pan. How many equal-size squares of cornbread does he cut in each pan?

15. _____

16. Aubrey has 15 dimes, 25 pennies, and 70 half-dollars in his coin collection. He has 6 rare dimes, 12 rare pennies, and 2 rare half-dollars. What fraction of his coins are rare coins?

16. _____

17. The florist begins receiving orders at 8:00 A.M. It takes him 2 hours each to fill two orders. At what time does the florist finish filling the two orders?

17. _____

18. Jake waits tables at his family's restaurant. He makes $15 per afternoon plus $3 in tips for every table he waits. On Saturday afternoon he made $75. How many tables did he serve?

18. _____

Name _____ Date _____

Chapter Extended-Response Test

Demonstrate your knowledge by giving a clear, concise solution to each problem. Be sure to include all relevant drawings and justify your answers. You may show your solution in more than one way or investigate beyond the requirements of the problem. If necessary, record your answer on another piece of paper.

1. a. Define the term fraction.

b. Define the terms numerator and denominator and explain how they are related.

2. Would you round $3\frac{1}{4}$ to 3 or 4? Explain your reasoning.

3. a. Explain in your own words how to rename an improper fraction as a mixed number. Provide an example.

b. Explain how to rename a mixed number as an improper fraction. Provide an example.

Name _____ Date _____

Cumulative Test Practice Chapters 1–8

Test Example

The Myers family made sandwiches for dinner with a loaf of bread. There were 16 slices of bread in the loaf originally. After dinner, $\frac{1}{4}$ of the loaf remained. How many slices of bread had been eaten?

    A. 10 slices   **C.** 13 slices

    B. 12 slices   **D.** 14 slices

Read the Test Item

You need to find the number of slices of bread that were eaten.

Solve the Test Item

First find how many slices are left. Then subtract this number from 16 to find the number of slices that were eaten.

$\frac{1}{4}$ of 16 is 4. Four slices remained, so 12 slices were eaten.

The answer is B.

Choose the best answer.

1. Two out of every 10 students in Mr. Dominguez's class has red hair. Which fraction is less than $\frac{2}{10}$?

    A. $\frac{5}{10}$ **B.** $\frac{4}{10}$ **C.** $\frac{3}{10}$ **D.** $\frac{1}{10}$

1. _____

2. There are 9 people in line at the water fountain. $\frac{1}{3}$ of these people are female. How many females are waiting in line?

    F. 1   **G.** 2   **H.** 3   **J.** 4

2. _____

Name _____ Date _____

Cumulative Test Practice (continued)

3. The line graph shows the number of airplane trips Beth took each year. Which statement about the data shown on the graph is true?

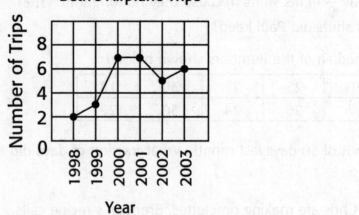

Beth's Airplane Trips

A. Beth took 2 trips in 2000.
B. 10 years are covered by the graph.
C. Beth took 6 trips in 2003.
D. Beth took the most trips in 1999.

3. _____

4. What is the mode of the following set of numbers?
8, 10, 5, 5, 8, 11, 8, 3

  F. 11   **G.** 8   **H.** 5   **J.** 3   **4.** _____

5. Carlos had 98 books on his bookshelf. There are 14 books on each shelf. How many shelves does Carlos have?

  A. 7   **B.** 6   **C.** 5   **D.** 4   **5.** _____

6. Which letter on the number line identifies the location of −3?

```
          A      B  C  D
  ◄──┼───┼───┼──┼──┼──┼───┼───┼──►
          −5            −1
```

  F. A   **G.** B   **H.** C   **J.** D   **6.** _____

7. Kira read 97 pages of a book last night, which was $\frac{2}{5}$ of the book. What decimal represents the fraction of the book that she read?

  A. 0.2   **B.** 0.3   **C.** 0.4   **D.** 0.5   **7.** _____

8

Cumulative Test Practice   *(continued)*

8. If $v = 7$, what is the value of $4v - 11$?

    F. 17   **G.** 15   **H.** 11   **J.** 7

8. _____

9. Paul gives away $\frac{4}{9}$ of his shirts because they no longer fit. What fraction of his shirts did Paul keep?

9. _____

10. What is the median of the numbers shown below?

20	25	21	30	18
17	26	24	30	22

10. _____

11. It snowed 6 out of 30 days last month. What fraction of days did it not snow?

11. _____

12. Brendan and Chris are making omelettes. Brendan's recipe calls for $\frac{3}{4}$-cup of cheese. Chris's recipe calls for $\frac{6}{8}$-cup of cheese. What is the relationship between the two fractions?

12. _____

13. What is the mode of the numbers shown below?

67	90	82
86	78	90

13. _____

14. Randy and Phil run a 100-meter race. Randy's time is 16.041 seconds and Phil's time is 16.149 seconds. Who won the race?

14. _____

15. A test has 100 questions. Rafael answers 85 of the questions correctly. What decimal represents the part of the questions Rafael answered correctly?

15. _____

16. Find the value of x to make the fractions equivalent. $\frac{3}{x} = \frac{12}{20}$

16. _____

Student Recording Sheet

Use this recording sheet with pages 368–369 of the Student Edition.

Read each question. Then fill in the correct answer.

1. Ⓐ Ⓑ Ⓒ Ⓓ   10. _____

2. Ⓕ Ⓖ Ⓗ Ⓙ   11. _____

3. Ⓐ Ⓑ Ⓒ Ⓓ   12. _____

4. Ⓕ Ⓖ Ⓗ Ⓙ   _____

     _____

5. Ⓐ Ⓑ Ⓒ Ⓓ

6. Ⓕ Ⓖ Ⓗ Ⓙ

7. Ⓐ Ⓑ Ⓒ Ⓓ

8. Ⓕ Ⓖ Ⓗ Ⓙ

9. Ⓐ Ⓑ Ⓒ Ⓓ

Assessment

Answers (Graphic Organizer and Anticipation Guide)

Graphic Organizer

Name _____ Date _____

Use this graphic organizer to take notes on Chapter 8: Develop Fraction Concepts. Fill in the missing information.

How do I ...	Instructions	Examples
... write a mixed number as an improper fraction?	**Mulitply the whole number by the denominator. Add the numerator. Write the sum over the original denominator.**	$5\frac{1}{3} = \frac{(5 \times 3) + 1}{3}$ $= \frac{16}{3}$
... rename an improper fraction as a mixed number?	**Divide the numerator by the denominator. Write the remainder as a fraction with the divisor as the denominator.**	$\frac{5}{3} = 3\overline{)5}$ $= 1\frac{2}{3}$
... use a number line to compare fractions?	**Remember that numbers to the right are greater than numbers to the left.**	$\frac{4}{6} > \frac{2}{6}$
... round fractions?	**Use a number line or round fractions mentally.**	$\frac{5}{8}$ rounds to $\frac{1}{2}$

Anticipation Guide

Name _____ Date _____

Develop Fraction Concepts

STEP 1   Before you begin Chapter 8

- Read each statement.
- Decide whether you agree (A) or disagree (D) with the statement.
- Write A or D in the first column OR if you are not sure whether you agree or disagree, write NS (not sure).

STEP 1 A, D, or NS	Statement	STEP 2 A or D
	1. $\frac{10}{9}$ is an improper fraction.	A
	2. A fraction means to divide.	A
	3. A mixed number has a whole number and a fraction.	A
	4. $\frac{7}{12}$ is an improper fraction.	D
	5. A fraction is a number that represents part of a whole or part of a set.	A
	6. $\frac{11}{3}$ is a mixed number.	D
	7. An improper fraction is converted to a mixed number by multiplying and adding.	D
	8. In the fraction $\frac{6}{10}$, 10 is the denominator.	A
	9. In the fraction $\frac{3}{12}$, 3 is the denominator.	D
	10. In the fraction $\frac{3}{4}$, 3 is the numerator.	A

STEP 2   After you complete Chapter 8

- Reread each statement and complete the last column by entering an A (agree) or a D (disagree).
- Did any of your opinions about the statements change from the first column?
- For those statements that you mark with a D, use a separate sheet of paper to explain why you disagree. Use examples, if possible.

Chapter Resources

Answers

Answers (Lesson 8–1)

8-1

Name _____ Date _____

Skills Practice

Fractions and Division

Represent each situation using a **fraction**. Then solve.

1. Mr. Janson has 3 jars of soup to divide among 4 people. How much soup will each person get?

$\frac{3}{4}$; **Each person gets** $\frac{3}{4}$ **of**

the soup.

2. Andrew shares his suitcase with his two brothers on vacation. How much space in the suitcase will Andrew and his brothers each have?

$\frac{1}{3}$; **Each person gets** $\frac{1}{3}$ **of**

the space in the suitcase.

3. Two small pizzas are shared by three people. How much pizza does each person get?

$\frac{2}{3}$; **Each person gets** $\frac{2}{3}$ **pizza.**

4. One container of paint is used to paint 7 tables. How much paint did each table use?

$\frac{1}{7}$; **Each table used** $\frac{1}{7}$

container of paint.

5. Five cupcakes are divided among 4 people. How many cupcakes does each person get?

$\frac{5}{4}$; **Each person gets** $\frac{5}{4}$ **or**

$1\frac{1}{4}$ **cupcakes.**

6. Four loaves of bread are divided equally among three students. How much bread will each student get?

$\frac{4}{3}$; **Each person gets** $\frac{4}{3}$ **or**

$1\frac{1}{3}$ **of a loaf.**

8-1

Name _____ Date _____

Reteach

Fractions and Division

Kelly, Jose, Jason, and Melanie are sharing 1 pizza. How much pizza does each person get?

A **fraction** is a number that names equal parts of a whole or parts of a group. A fraction represents division. If 1 is divided into 4 equal parts, one part is $\frac{1}{4}$.

The **numerator** is the number above the bar in a fraction. The **denominator** is the number below the bar in a fraction.

Words: 1 pizza divided among 4 people

Symbols: 1 ÷ 4

Fraction:

1 pizza → 1 ← numerator

4 people → 4 ← denominator

Model:

The fraction $\frac{1}{4}$ means that each person gets $\frac{1}{4}$ of the pizza.

Represent each situation using a fraction. Then solve.

1. At the picnic there are 3 pieces of fruit for 4 people. How many pieces of fruit will each person receive?

$\frac{3}{4}$; **Each person gets** $\frac{3}{4}$ a

piece of fruit.

2. Six bags of trail mix are divided among 17 people. How much of the trail mix did each person receive?

$\frac{6}{17}$; **Each person gets** $\frac{6}{17}$ **of**

the trail mix.

8-1

Name _____ Date _____

Problem-Solving Practice
Fractions and Division

Represent each situation using a fraction. Then solve.

1. Elena drank 5 bottles of water over 7 days. How much water did Elena drink each day?

   $\frac{5}{7}$; **Elena drank $\frac{5}{7}$ bottle each day.**

2. Molly is slicing 3 pizzas into equal slices so that 8 people can each have a piece. How much pizza does each person receive?

   $\frac{3}{8}$; **Each person gets $\frac{3}{8}$ pizza.**

3. The Littleton family drinks 2 gallons of milk in 5 days. How many gallons do they drink each day?

   $\frac{2}{5}$; **The Littleton family drinks $\frac{2}{5}$ gal each day.**

4. Three gallons of paint are used to paint 16 wooden signs. How much paint did each sign use?

   $\frac{3}{16}$; **Each sign used $\frac{3}{16}$ gal of paint.**

5. Three bags of packing peanuts are used to fill 2 boxes. How many bags of packing peanuts does each box use?

   $\frac{3}{2}$; **Each box uses $\frac{3}{2}$ or $1\frac{1}{2}$ bags of packing peanuts.**

6. Nine yards of ribbon are used to make 2 bows. How many yards of ribbon does each bow use?

   $\frac{9}{2}$; **Each bow uses $\frac{9}{2}$ or $4\frac{1}{2}$ yd of ribbon.**

8-1

Name _____ Date _____

Homework Practice
Fractions and Division

Represent each situation using a fraction. Then solve.

1. Three bags of soil are used to fill 4 flowerpots. How many cups of soil does each flowerpot use?

   $\frac{3}{4}$; **Each flowerpot gets $\frac{3}{4}$ cups of soil.**

2. Three people equally share five lemon squares. How many lemon squares does each person receive?

   $\frac{5}{3}$; **Each person receives $\frac{5}{3}$ or $1\frac{2}{3}$ lemon squares.**

3. In science class there are 5 cups of water to be used for the experiments. If six students work on the experiments, how many cups of water does each student receive?

   $\frac{5}{6}$; **Each student receives $\frac{5}{6}$ cup of water.**

4. Four yards of fabric are used to make five craft projects. How many yards of fabric does each craft project use?

   $\frac{4}{5}$; **Each project used $\frac{4}{5}$ yard of fabric.**

Spiral Review

Which type of graph would you use to display the data in each table? Write bar graph, line graph, or pictograph.

5. Brandon surveyed his classmates to find their favorite sport. Which type of graph should you use to display the data? Which sport is most popular?

Favorite Sports	
Basketball	9
Baseball	6
Football	18
Soccer	7
Lacrosse	3

   Pictograph or Bar graph; Football

6. The following table shows the height of five students. Which type of graph should you use? What is the median of these heights?

Student Heights	
Name	Height (in.)
Jennifer	58
Troy	55
Bianca	49
Rosa	50
Anna	42

   Bar graph; 50 in.

Answers (Lessons 8–1 and 8–2)

Name _____ Date _____

8-2 Reteach
Improper Fractions

An **improper fraction** is a fraction that has a numerator that is greater than or equal to its denominator.	A **mixed number** has a whole number and a fraction.
Example: $\frac{7}{4}$ $\frac{8}{6}$ $\frac{9}{2}$ $\frac{2}{2}$	**Example:** $5\frac{1}{3}$ $3\frac{1}{2}$ $6\frac{2}{5}$

Renaming an Improper Fraction

To write an improper fraction as a mixed number, divide the numerator by the denominator. Write the remainder as a fraction of the divisor.

Example: $\frac{8}{3} = \begin{array}{r} 2R2 \\ 3\overline{)8} \\ -6 \\ \hline 2 \end{array} \rightarrow 2\frac{2}{3}$ **Example:** $\frac{19}{4} = \begin{array}{r} 4R3 \\ 4\overline{)19} \\ -16 \\ \hline 3 \end{array} \rightarrow 4\frac{3}{4}$

Write each improper fraction as a mixed number.

1. $\frac{15}{2}$ $7\frac{1}{2}$ 2. $\frac{18}{5}$ $3\frac{3}{5}$ 3. $\frac{9}{4}$ $2\frac{1}{4}$

4. $\frac{4}{3}$ $1\frac{1}{3}$ 5. $\frac{7}{2}$ $3\frac{1}{2}$ 6. $\frac{19}{6}$ $3\frac{1}{6}$

7. $\frac{17}{2}$ $8\frac{1}{2}$ 8. $\frac{9}{8}$ $1\frac{1}{8}$ 9. $\frac{13}{2}$ $6\frac{1}{2}$

10. $\frac{7}{4}$ $1\frac{3}{4}$ 11. $\frac{27}{7}$ $3\frac{6}{7}$ 12. $\frac{29}{8}$ $3\frac{5}{8}$

13. $\frac{23}{3}$ $7\frac{2}{3}$ 14. $\frac{33}{5}$ $6\frac{3}{5}$ 15. $\frac{19}{2}$ $9\frac{1}{2}$

Grade 5   13   Chapter 8

Name _____ Date _____

8-1 Enrich
Fractions and Division

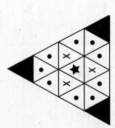

The large triangle is made of four rows of small triangles. Some of the small triangles have three corners that are on the large triangle. Shade each of these small triangles.

1. Some of the triangles have exactly one corner that is on the large triangle. Draw an X in each of these small triangles.

2. Some of the triangles have exactly two corners that are on the large triangle. Draw a dot in each of these small triangles.

3. Some of the triangles have exactly one corner that is on the large triangle. Draw an X in each of these small triangles.

4. Some of the triangles have no corners that are on the large triangle. Draw a star in each of these small triangles.

5. What fraction of the small triangles is shaded? $\frac{3}{16}$

6. What fraction of the small triangles has a dot? $\frac{9}{16}$

7. What fraction of the small triangles has an X? $\frac{3}{16}$

8. What fraction of the small triangles has a star? $\frac{1}{16}$

9. What fraction of the small triangles has at least one corner that is on the larger triangle? $\frac{15}{16}$

Grade 5   12   Chapter 8

Answers (Lesson 8-2)

Chapter Resources

8-2 Skills Practice
Improper Fractions

Write each improper fraction as a mixed number.

1. $\frac{13}{2}$ $6\frac{1}{2}$
2. $\frac{5}{3}$ $1\frac{2}{3}$
3. $\frac{19}{3}$ $6\frac{1}{3}$
4. $\frac{3}{2}$ $1\frac{1}{2}$
5. $\frac{17}{4}$ $4\frac{1}{4}$
6. $\frac{31}{5}$ $6\frac{1}{5}$
7. $\frac{16}{5}$ $3\frac{1}{5}$
8. $\frac{4}{3}$ $1\frac{1}{3}$
9. $\frac{13}{9}$ $1\frac{4}{9}$
10. $\frac{11}{3}$ $3\frac{2}{3}$
11. $\frac{49}{8}$ $6\frac{1}{8}$
12. $\frac{8}{5}$ $1\frac{3}{5}$
13. $\frac{44}{9}$ $4\frac{8}{9}$
14. $\frac{12}{11}$ $1\frac{1}{11}$
15. $\frac{38}{7}$ $5\frac{3}{7}$
16. $\frac{20}{7}$ $2\frac{6}{7}$
17. $\frac{41}{8}$ $5\frac{1}{8}$
18. $\frac{10}{7}$ $1\frac{3}{7}$
19. $\frac{19}{5}$ $3\frac{4}{5}$
20. $\frac{7}{3}$ $2\frac{1}{3}$
21. $\frac{29}{9}$ $3\frac{2}{9}$
22. $\frac{51}{8}$ $6\frac{3}{8}$
23. $\frac{17}{6}$ $2\frac{5}{6}$
24. $\frac{9}{2}$ $4\frac{1}{2}$
25. $\frac{45}{8}$ $5\frac{5}{8}$
26. $\frac{68}{7}$ $9\frac{5}{7}$
27. $\frac{12}{5}$ $2\frac{2}{5}$
28. $\frac{22}{3}$ $7\frac{1}{3}$
29. $\frac{49}{6}$ $8\frac{1}{6}$
30. $\frac{28}{3}$ $9\frac{1}{3}$

Grade 5   14   Chapter 8

8-2 Homework Practice
Improper Fractions

Write each improper fraction as a mixed number.

1. $\frac{11}{6}$ $1\frac{5}{6}$
2. $\frac{13}{4}$ $3\frac{1}{4}$
3. $\frac{41}{7}$ $5\frac{6}{7}$
4. $\frac{19}{4}$ $4\frac{3}{4}$
5. $\frac{5}{2}$ $2\frac{1}{2}$
6. $\frac{38}{5}$ $7\frac{3}{5}$
7. $\frac{9}{2}$ $4\frac{1}{2}$
8. $\frac{14}{3}$ $4\frac{2}{3}$
9. $\frac{39}{8}$ $4\frac{7}{8}$
10. $\frac{25}{6}$ $4\frac{1}{6}$
11. $\frac{22}{5}$ $4\frac{2}{5}$
12. $\frac{17}{4}$ $4\frac{1}{4}$
13. $\frac{80}{9}$ $8\frac{8}{9}$
14. $\frac{13}{10}$ $1\frac{3}{10}$
15. $\frac{67}{7}$ $9\frac{4}{7}$
16. $\frac{71}{8}$ $8\frac{7}{8}$
17. $\frac{8}{3}$ $2\frac{2}{3}$
18. $\frac{14}{5}$ $2\frac{4}{5}$
19. $\frac{28}{3}$ $9\frac{1}{3}$
20. $\frac{61}{7}$ $8\frac{5}{7}$
21. $\frac{13}{6}$ $2\frac{1}{6}$

Spiral Review

Represent each situation using a fraction. Then solve. (Lesson 8–1)

22. Eight people equally share 3 pizzas. How much pizza does each person recieve? $\frac{3}{8}$; Each person receives $\frac{3}{8}$ of a pizza.

23. In art class, there are 5 sheets of drawing paper for 9 people. How much paper will each person receive? $\frac{5}{9}$; Each person receives $\frac{5}{9}$ of the paper.

24. Five gallons of punch fill 3 punch bowls equally. How much punch will be in each punch bowl? $\frac{5}{3}$; Each punch bowl will hold $\frac{5}{3}$ or $1\frac{2}{3}$ gallons of punch.

Grade 5   15   Chapter 8

Copyright © Macmillan/McGraw-Hill, a division of The McGraw-Hill Companies, Inc.

Answers

Grade 5   A5   Chapter 8

8-2

Name _____ Date _____

Enrich
Understanding Fractions

Match each improper fraction below a blank to a mixed number with a letter below. Write the letter in the blank to complete a quote by Willy Wonka from the book *Charlie and the Chocolate Factory* by Roald Dahl.

"A little nonsense now and then

I	S	R	E	L	I	S	H	E	D
$\frac{21}{10}$	$\frac{17}{3}$	$\frac{22}{6}$	$\frac{26}{8}$	$\frac{49}{5}$	$\frac{21}{10}$	$\frac{17}{3}$	$\frac{13}{3}$	$\frac{26}{8}$	$\frac{50}{8}$

B	Y	T	H	E	W	I	S	E	S	T
$\frac{44}{6}$	$\frac{34}{4}$	$\frac{22}{9}$	$\frac{13}{3}$	$\frac{26}{8}$	$\frac{19}{4}$	$\frac{21}{10}$	$\frac{17}{3}$	$\frac{26}{8}$	$\frac{17}{3}$	$\frac{22}{9}$

M	E	N
$\frac{20}{3}$	$\frac{26}{8}$	$\frac{8}{5}$

$N = 1\frac{3}{5}$ $S = 5\frac{2}{3}$ $I = 2\frac{1}{10}$ $D = 6\frac{2}{8}$

$M = 6\frac{2}{3}$ $W = 4\frac{3}{4}$ $H = 4\frac{1}{3}$ $T = 2\frac{4}{9}$

$E = 3\frac{2}{8}$ $L = 9\frac{4}{5}$ $R = 3\frac{4}{6}$ $Y = 8\frac{2}{4}$

$B = 7\frac{2}{6}$

How did you change $3\frac{2}{8}$ into an improper fraction?
Sample answer: By multiplying 8 and 3, then adding 2 to get $\frac{26}{8}$.

8-2

Name _____ Date _____

Problem-Solving Practice
Improper Fractions

Solve.

1. Sixty-three students have signed up for summer soccer camp. If each soccer team can have 11 players, how many teams can be formed? Write the answer as a mixed number and as a remainder. Explain what the remainder means.

   $5\frac{8}{11}$; 5 R8; 5 teams can be formed and 8 students will be left over.

2. Taye rode his bicycle 47 miles in 3 hours. Write the number of miles ridden each hour as a mixed number.

   $15\frac{2}{3}$

3. Shawna is decorating a scrapbook page with stickers. She has 40 stickers and 6 stickers will fit on one scrapbook page. How many pages can she fill with stickers? Write the answer as a mixed number and as a remainder. Explain what the remainder means.

   $6\frac{2}{3}$; 6 R4; 6 pages will be full of stickers and the seventh page will be $\frac{2}{3}$ full of stickers.

4. Rodney is putting away test tubes in science class. He has 50 test tubes and 12 will fit on each rack. How many racks will Rodney fill? Write the answer as a mixed number.

   $4\frac{1}{6}$

5. Leah is assembling gift bags for her birthday party. Nine friends are coming to the party. Leah has 58 items for all the gift bags. How many items should she put in each bag? Will there be any items left over?

   She can out 6 items in each bag, and she will have 4 items left over.

6. Arvin is making a fruit snack for himself and his 3 brothers. If he has 35 apple slices, how many will each brother get? Write the answer as a mixed number and as a remainder. Explain what the remainder means.

   $8\frac{3}{4}$; 8 R3; each brother will get 8 apple slices and there will be 3 left over.

Answers (Lesson 8–3)

8-3 Reteach
Use Logical Reasoning (continued)

Name _____ Date _____

Solve. Use logical reasoning.

2. Barbara can swim four laps in 2 minutes. How long does it take her to swim one lap?

30 seconds

3. The park has 3 more maple trees than spruce trees. There are 13 maple and spruce trees in all. How many maple trees are there?

8

4. Leonard can run a mile in 9 minutes. Alicia can run a mile in 7 minutes. If they run together, how long after Alicia finishes will Leonard finish?

2 minutes

5. Carl is making a garden. He buys 3 packets of violet seeds for $0.35 each, 2 packets of marigold seeds for $0.50 each, one bag of soil for $1.50, and a new pair of gloves for $4.50. How much money will Carl spend in all?

$8.05

6. Ramona can ride her bike 1 mile in 5 minutes. How long will it take her to ride 4 miles?

20 minutes

7. Ronald and his brother are going to visit their grandmother. If their father drives 45 miles an hour, it will take 2 hours to get there. How far do they have to travel?

90 miles

8-3 Reteach
Problem-Solving Strategy: Use Logical Reasoning

Name _____ Date _____

Use the logical reasoning strategy to solve problems.

The table shows the times of some women who competed in the Snowboard Cross event in the 2006 Winter Olympics. How much less time did it take Tanja Freiden than Yuka Fujimori?

Athlete	Time (minutes)
Lindsey Jacobellis	1 min 29 sec
Tanja Frieden	1 min 30 sec
Katharina Himmler	1 min 43 sec
Yuka Fujimori	1 min 48 sec

Understand

What facts do you know?

Tanja Frieden's time was 1 minute 30 seconds. Yuka Fujimori's time was 1 minute 48 seconds.

What do you need to find?

How much less time it took Tanja Frieden than it took Yuka Fujimori.

Plan

You can subtract 1 minute 30 seconds from 1 minute 48 seconds to find the answer.

Solve

Use your plan to solve the problem.

1 min 48 sec – 1 min 30 sec = 18 sec

Check

Look back. 1 minute 30 seconds + 18 seconds = 1 minute 48 seconds. So, you know the answer is correct.

Solve. Use logical reasoning.

1. Miss Graham's class is buying supplies for a party. They need to buy 3 packs of balloons, 2 rolls of streamers, and 1 set of wall decorations. Use the chart below to find out how much each item costs. How much will their party supplies cost in all?

Item	Cost
Pack of Balloons	$1.37
Roll of Streamers	$0.99
Set of Wall Decorations	$8.50

$14.59

8-3 Skills Practice
Problem-Solving Strategy

Name _____ Date _____

Solve. Use logical reasoning.

1. Julia can make 2 pieces of toast in 3 minutes. How long will it take her to make 8 pieces of toast?
12 minutes

2. Jeff has saved $40.50. He wants to buy a new pair of shoes which cost $35.75. The sales tax on these shoes is $2.50. How much money will Jeff have left over after making this purchase?
$2.25

3. In the school choir there are 3 more boys than girls. There are 13 boys and girls in the choir in all. How many boys are there in the choir?
8 boys

4. The following chart shows some of the countries who earned the most gold medals in the 2006 Winter Olympics. How many more medals did Austria win than Estonia?
6 gold medals

Country	Number of Gold Medals
Germany	11
Austria	9
South Korea	6
Estonia	3

5. Louise, Jacqueline, and Martha ran a one-mile race. Louise finished in 8.47 minutes, Jacqueline finished in 9.32 minutes, and Martha finished in 8.34 minutes. How much time passed between Martha's finish and Jacqueline's finish?
0.98 minutes

6. Shamera and Diana have played 14 games of checkers. Shamera has won 2 more games than Diana. How many games has Diana won?
6

Grade 5   20   Chapter 8

8-3 Homework Practice
Problem-Solving Strategy

Name _____ Date _____

Solve. Use logical reasoning.

1. For a science lesson, Mr. Miller asked his students to each bring in a leaf or a pinecone. The students brought in 21 leaves and pinecones in all. There were 5 more leaves than pinecones. How many pinecones did the students bring in?
8

2. Jenna can swim one lap in the pool in 36 seconds. How long will it take her to swim 3 laps?
108 seconds

3. There are 16 ounces in 1 pound. How many ounces are there in 3 pounds?
48 ounces

4. Marcus is practicing for the basketball team. The chart below shows the number of minutes he has practiced for each of the last 4 days. If the pattern continues, how many minutes will he practice on the fifth day?
90 minutes

Day	Time (in minutes)
One	30
Two	45
Three	60
Four	75
Five	___

Spiral Review
Write each improper fraction as a mixed number. (Lesson 8–2)

5. $\frac{7}{2}$ $3\frac{1}{2}$
6. $\frac{5}{3}$ $1\frac{2}{3}$
7. $\frac{12}{5}$ $2\frac{2}{5}$
8. $\frac{15}{2}$ $7\frac{1}{2}$
9. $\frac{18}{7}$ $2\frac{4}{7}$
10. $\frac{9}{4}$ $2\frac{1}{4}$

Grade 5   21   Chapter 8

Name _____ Date _____

8-4 Reteach
Mixed Numbers

A **mixed number** is made up of a whole number and a fraction.
An **improper fraction** is a fraction in which the numerator is greater than or equal to the denominator.

Write $2\frac{2}{3}$ as an improper fraction.

Step 1
Multiply the whole number by the denominator.

$2\frac{2}{3} \longrightarrow 2 \times 3 = 6$

Step 2
Add the numerator to the product.

$6 + 2 = 8$

Step 3
Write the sum over the denominator.

$2\frac{2}{3} = \frac{8}{3}$

Write each mixed number as an improper fraction.

1. $2\frac{2}{7}$ $\frac{16}{7}$
2. $5\frac{3}{4}$ $\frac{23}{4}$
3. $6\frac{5}{8}$ $\frac{53}{8}$

4. $3\frac{4}{10}$ $\frac{34}{10}$
5. $9\frac{1}{3}$ $\frac{28}{3}$
6. $4\frac{4}{5}$ $\frac{24}{5}$

7. $1\frac{1}{8}$ $\frac{9}{8}$
8. $3\frac{1}{2}$ $\frac{7}{2}$
9. $2\frac{2}{5}$ $\frac{12}{5}$

10. $2\frac{2}{3}$ $\frac{8}{3}$
11. $1\frac{3}{4}$ $\frac{7}{4}$
12. $1\frac{1}{5}$ $\frac{6}{5}$

13. $6\frac{2}{3}$ $\frac{20}{3}$
14. $3\frac{2}{5}$ $\frac{17}{5}$
15. $4\frac{1}{2}$ $\frac{9}{2}$

16. $1\frac{4}{5}$ $\frac{9}{5}$
17. $3\frac{5}{8}$ $\frac{29}{8}$
18. $2\frac{2}{3}$ $\frac{8}{3}$

23

Name _____ Date _____

8-3 Enrich
Egyptian Fractions

The ancient Egyptians wrote numbers using different symbols than those we use today. The ancient Egyptian symbols for 100, 10, and 1 are shown below.

The Egyptian symbol for the number 215 is shown at the right.

A *unit fraction* has 1 as its numerator. Ancient Egyptians wrote all fraction as unit fractions. To show a fraction, they used the symbol for a mouth ⃝ above the denominator. The ancient Egyptian symbol for $\frac{1}{12}$ is shown at the right.

Write the ancient Egyptian symbol for each number.

1. 16
2. 24
3. 131

Write the ancient Egyptian symbol for each fraction.

4. $\frac{1}{3}$
5. $\frac{1}{10}$
6. $\frac{1}{17}$

7. $\frac{1}{25}$
8. $\frac{1}{110}$
9. $\frac{1}{201}$

Write each Egyptian fraction as it would be written today.

10. $\frac{1}{5}$
11. $\frac{1}{20}$
12. $\frac{1}{100}$
13. $\frac{1}{2}$

22

Name _____ Date _____

8-4

Homework Practice
Mixed Numbers

Write each mixed number as an improper fraction.

1. $2\frac{3}{4}$ $\frac{11}{4}$ 2. $5\frac{1}{6}$ $\frac{31}{6}$ 3. $8\frac{1}{2}$ $\frac{17}{2}$

4. $3\frac{2}{3}$ $\frac{11}{3}$ 5. $7\frac{2}{5}$ $\frac{37}{5}$ 6. $1\frac{9}{10}$ $\frac{19}{10}$

7. $4\frac{7}{8}$ $\frac{39}{8}$ 8. $6\frac{5}{7}$ $\frac{47}{7}$ 9. $1\frac{8}{9}$ $\frac{17}{9}$

10. $3\frac{12}{17}$ $\frac{63}{17}$ 11. $2\frac{1}{10}$ $\frac{21}{10}$ 12. $5\frac{5}{13}$ $\frac{70}{13}$

13. $1\frac{1}{2}$ $\frac{3}{2}$ 14. $7\frac{1}{3}$ $\frac{22}{3}$ 15. 3 $\frac{3}{1}$

16. $3\frac{1}{2}$ $\frac{7}{2}$ 17. $4\frac{2}{3}$ $\frac{14}{3}$ 18. 8 $\frac{8}{1}$

19. $2\frac{3}{5}$ $\frac{13}{5}$ 20. $5\frac{3}{4}$ $\frac{23}{4}$ 21. $2\frac{5}{8}$ $\frac{21}{8}$

22. $1\frac{29}{35}$ $\frac{64}{35}$ 23. $6\frac{1}{3}$ $\frac{19}{3}$ 24. $5\frac{1}{2}$ $\frac{11}{2}$

25. $3\frac{7}{10}$ $\frac{37}{10}$ 26. $4\frac{1}{2}$ $\frac{9}{2}$ 27. $4\frac{1}{10}$ $\frac{41}{10}$

28. $5\frac{2}{5}$ $\frac{27}{5}$ 29. $8\frac{3}{4}$ $\frac{35}{4}$ 30. $2\frac{3}{5}$ $\frac{13}{5}$

Spiral Review
Solve. Use logical reasoning.

31. A shipment of boxes weighs 40 pounds. There are 8 boxes and each weighs the same number of pounds. How much does each box weigh?   **5 pounds**

32. Mrs. Cooper's fifth-grade class has 11 more girls than boys. There are 35 students in all. How many girls are there?   **23 girls**

Name _____ Date _____

8-4

Skills Practice
Mixed Numbers

Write each mixed number as an improper fraction.

1. $3\frac{1}{2}$ $\frac{7}{2}$ 2. $5\frac{3}{4}$ $\frac{23}{4}$ 3. $6\frac{7}{8}$ $\frac{55}{8}$

4. $5\frac{5}{12}$ $\frac{65}{12}$ 5. $4\frac{1}{6}$ $\frac{25}{6}$ 6. $6\frac{2}{3}$ $\frac{20}{3}$

7. $12\frac{2}{3}$ $\frac{38}{3}$ 8. $10\frac{23}{100}$ $\frac{1,023}{100}$ 9. $9\frac{1}{4}$ $\frac{37}{4}$

10. $8\frac{2}{5}$ $\frac{42}{5}$ 11. $25\frac{1}{4}$ $\frac{101}{4}$ 12. $22\frac{1}{2}$ $\frac{45}{2}$

13. $6\frac{4}{5}$ $\frac{34}{5}$ 14. $4\frac{3}{10}$ $\frac{43}{10}$ 15. $6\frac{1}{100}$ $\frac{601}{100}$

16. $7\frac{5}{8}$ $\frac{61}{8}$ 17. $6\frac{3}{8}$ $\frac{51}{8}$ 18. $3\frac{9}{100}$ $\frac{309}{100}$

19. $5\frac{5}{6}$ $\frac{35}{6}$ 20. $9\frac{3}{17}$ $\frac{156}{17}$ 21. $25\frac{1}{3}$ $\frac{76}{3}$

22. $5\frac{2}{9}$ $\frac{47}{9}$ 23. $12\frac{2}{3}$ $\frac{38}{3}$ 24. $5\frac{3}{7}$ $\frac{38}{7}$

25. $6\frac{4}{9}$ $\frac{58}{9}$ 26. $10\frac{1}{18}$ $\frac{181}{18}$ 27. $5\frac{5}{12}$ $\frac{65}{12}$

28. $6\frac{2}{13}$ $\frac{80}{13}$ 29. $25\frac{4}{5}$ $\frac{129}{5}$ 30. $20\frac{5}{6}$ $\frac{125}{6}$

Solve.

31. Tina spent $3\frac{1}{3}$ hours practicing the piano. Write this quantity as an improper fraction. $\frac{10}{3}$

32. Suppose you have $2\frac{1}{4}$ oranges. Write this quantity as an improper fraction. $\frac{9}{4}$

Answers (Lesson 8–4)

Left page (Problem-Solving Practice)

Name _____ Date _____

8-4

Problem-Solving Practice

Mixed Numbers

Solve.

1. During the holiday break, Anthony read one book, and half of another book. How many books did he read?

   $1\frac{1}{2}$ **books**

2. Sam's family ate 2 pizzas. Then they ate 5 of the 8 slices of another pizza. How many pizzas did his family eat?

   $2\frac{5}{8}$

3. Hans ran 3 miles on the track. He took a break, then ran another $\frac{4}{5}$ mile. Write the number of miles Hans ran as an improper fraction.

   $\frac{19}{5}$ **miles**

4. Lindsey ran in a 10-kilometer race. This is equal to $6\frac{1}{5}$ miles. Write the number of miles Lindsey ran as an improper fraction.

   $\frac{31}{5}$ **miles**

5. Keisha is running on an indoor track where 8 laps equals one mile. If she runs 19 laps, how many miles is this? Write your answer as a mixed number and as an improper fraction.

   $2\frac{3}{8}; \frac{19}{8}$

6. Doug found that it takes 20 minutes to do 8 math problems. If he has 28 problems, how long will it take him to do them?

   1 hour and 10 minutes

Right page (Enrich)

Name _____ Date _____

8-4

Enrich

A Maze of Mixed Numbers

Solve A–N by rounding to the nearest whole number. Then find your way through the maze to reach the dot. When you come to a letter, choose the number that matches your answer. Follow the path until you reach the next intersection.

A. $2\frac{7}{8}$ **3**	B. $6\frac{1}{7}$ **6**	C. $3\frac{3}{4}$ **4**	D. $8\frac{2}{10}$ **8**
E. $9\frac{7}{9}$ **10**	F. $\frac{5}{6}$ **1**	G. $12\frac{5}{7}$ **13**	H. $20\frac{5}{7}$ **21**
I. $18\frac{2}{10}$ **18**	J. $16\frac{7}{9}$ **17**	K. $7\frac{3}{20}$ **7**	L. $1\frac{4}{5}$ **2**
M. $5\frac{2}{14}$ **5**	N. $14\frac{8}{10}$ **15**		

Answers

Answers (Lesson 8–5)

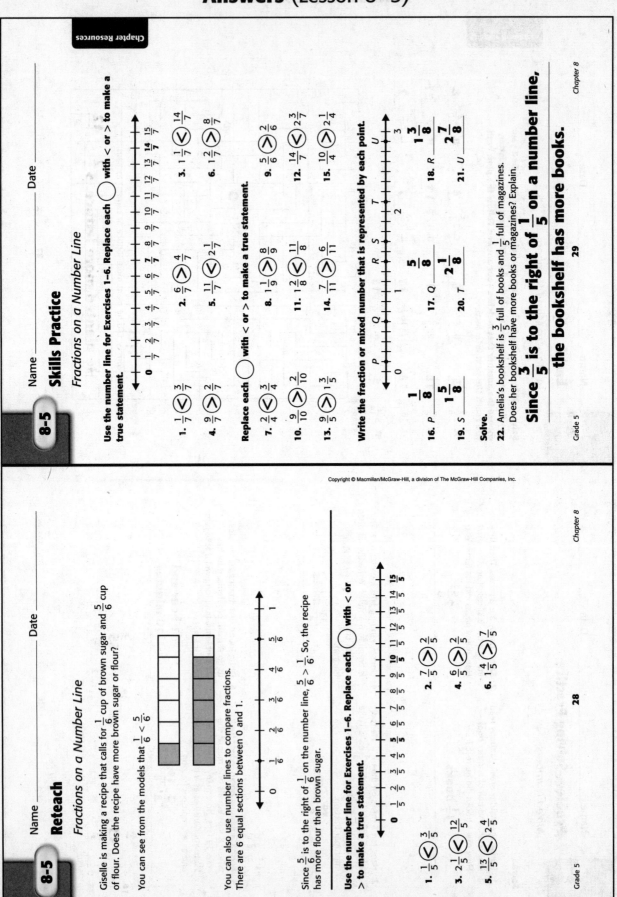

8-5

Name _____ Date _____

Skills Practice

Fractions on a Number Line

Use the number line for Exercises 1–6. Replace each ◯ with < or > to make a true statement.

0 1/7 2/7 3/7 4/7 5/7 6/7 7/7 8/7 9/7 10/7 11/7 12/7 13/7 **14/7** **15/7**

1. 1/7 ⟨<⟩ 3/7

2. 6/7 ⟨>⟩ 4/7

3. 1 1/7 ⟨<⟩ 14/7

4. 9/7 ⟨>⟩ 2/7

5. 11/7 ⟨<⟩ 2 1/7

6. 1 2/7 ⟨>⟩ 8/7

Replace each ◯ with < or > to make a true statement.

7. 2/4 ⟨<⟩ 3/4

8. 1 1/9 ⟨>⟩ 8/9

9. 5/6 ⟨>⟩ 2/6

10. 9/10 ⟨>⟩ 2/10

11. 1 2/8 ⟨<⟩ 11/8

12. 14/7 ⟨<⟩ 2 3/7

13. 9/5 ⟨>⟩ 1 3/5

14. 7/11 ⟨>⟩ 6/11

15. 10/4 ⟨>⟩ 2 1/4

Write the fraction or mixed number that is represented by each point.

P   Q   R   S   T   U

0   1   2   3

16. P 1/8

17. Q 5/8

18. R 1 3/8

19. S 1 5/8

20. T 2 1/8

21. U 2 7/8

Solve.

22. Amelia's bookshelf is 3/5 full of books and 1/5 full of magazines. Does her bookshelf have more books or magazines? Explain.

Since 3/5 is to the right of 1/5 on a number line, the bookshelf has more books.

8-5

Name _____ Date _____

Reteach

Fractions on a Number Line

Giselle is making a recipe that calls for 1/6 cup of brown sugar and 5/6 cup of flour. Does the recipe have more brown sugar or flour?

You can see from the models that 1/6 < 5/6.

You can also use number lines to compare fractions. There are 6 equal sections between 0 and 1.

0   1/6   2/6   3/6   4/6   5/6   1

Since 5/6 is to the right of 1/6 on the number line, 5/6 > 1/6. So, the recipe has more flour than brown sugar.

Use the number line for Exercises 1–6. Replace each ◯ with < or > to make a true statement.

0 1/5 2/5 3/5 4/5 5/5 6/5 7/5 8/5 9/5 10/5 11/5 12/5 13/5 14/5 15/5

1. 1/5 ⟨<⟩ 3/5

2. 7/5 ⟨>⟩ 2/5

3. 2 1/5 ⟨<⟩ 12/5

4. 6/5 ⟨>⟩ 2/5

5. 13/5 ⟨<⟩ 2 4/5

6. 1 4/5 ⟨>⟩ 7/5

Answers (Lesson 8–5)

Homework Practice 8-5
Fractions on a Number Line

Name _____ Date _____

Replace each ◯ with < or > to make a true statement.

1. $\frac{2}{3}$ ⃝> $\frac{5}{3}$
2. $3\frac{3}{8}$ ⃝< $\frac{28}{8}$
3. $\frac{3}{7}$ ⃝> $\frac{2}{7}$

4. $\frac{11}{9}$ ⃝< $1\frac{3}{9}$
5. $1\frac{2}{5}$ ⃝< $\frac{8}{5}$
6. $\frac{16}{7}$ ⃝< $2\frac{5}{7}$

7. $\frac{9}{4}$ ⃝> $1\frac{3}{4}$
8. $\frac{13}{10}$ ⃝> $1\frac{1}{10}$
9. $\frac{13}{8}$ ⃝< $2\frac{1}{8}$

Write the fraction or mixed number that is represented by each point.

```
  A  B  C  D  E  F
0 |        |        | 2
          1
```

10. A $\frac{3}{10}$
11. B $\frac{7}{10}$
12. C $1\frac{9}{10}$
13. D $1\frac{5}{10}$
14. E $1\frac{1}{10}$
15. F $2\frac{3}{10}$

Spiral Review
Write each mixed number as an improper fraction. (Lesson 8–4)

16. $2\frac{3}{5}$ $\frac{13}{5}$
17. $5\frac{1}{10}$ $\frac{51}{10}$

18. $4\frac{5}{8}$ $\frac{37}{8}$
19. $11\frac{4}{5}$ $\frac{59}{5}$

20. $6\frac{1}{7}$ $\frac{43}{7}$
21. $7\frac{2}{9}$ $\frac{65}{9}$

Grade 5   30   Chapter 8

Problem-Solving Practice 8-5
Fractions on a Number Line

Name _____ Date _____

Solve.

1. James walks $2\frac{1}{7}$ miles to school. Kiana walks $\frac{19}{7}$ miles to school. Who walks farther to school? Explain.

Kiana walks farther. $\frac{19}{7} > 2\frac{1}{7}$

2. Clarice lives $\frac{17}{8}$ miles from her grandmother's house and $2\frac{3}{8}$ miles from her aunt's house. Does Clarice live closer to her aunt or her grandmother? Explain. $\frac{17}{8} < 2\frac{3}{8}$

Clarice lives closer to her grandmother.

3. Henry's pet bird weighs $4\frac{3}{16}$ ounces and his pet kitten weighs $\frac{65}{16}$ ounces. Which pet weighs more? Explain.

Henry's pet bird weighs more. $4\frac{3}{16} > \frac{65}{16}$

4. A recipe for lemonade calls for $\frac{11}{4}$ cup lemon juice and $2\frac{1}{4}$ cup water. Does the recipe have more lemon juice or water? Explain.

The recipe has more lemon juice. $\frac{11}{4} > 2\frac{1}{4}$

5. Elina made a skirt using $3\frac{2}{5}$ yards of fabric. She made a dress using $\frac{17}{5}$ yards of fabric. Which item used more fabric? Explain.

The skirt and dress used the same amount of fabric. $3\frac{2}{5} = \frac{17}{5}$

6. Greg's dad planted $5\frac{2}{9}$ rows of his garden with lettuce. He planted $\frac{42}{9}$ rows of the garden with carrots. Did he plant more lettuce or carrots? Explain.

He planted more lettuce. $5\frac{2}{9} > \frac{42}{9}$

Grade 5   31   Chapter 8

Answers (Lessons 8–5 and 8–6)

8–5

Name _____ Date _____

Enrich

Unit Rates

A **unit rate** is a comparison of two quantities by division in which the denominator is 1.

Description	Rate	Unit Rate
riding a bicycle 23 miles in 2 hours	$\dfrac{23\text{ miles}}{2\text{ hours}}$	$\dfrac{23\text{ miles} \div 2}{2\text{ hours} \div 2} = \dfrac{11\frac{1}{2}\text{ miles}}{1\text{ hour}}$ $= 11\frac{1}{2}\text{ miles/hour}$
reading 14 pages in 8 minutes	$\dfrac{14\text{ pages}}{8\text{ minutes}}$	$\dfrac{14\text{ pages} \div 8}{8\text{ minutes} \div 8} = \dfrac{1\frac{3}{4}\text{ pages}}{1\text{ minute}}$ $= 1\frac{3}{4}\text{ pages/minute}$
earning $33 for babysitting 5 hours	$\dfrac{\$33}{5\text{ hours}}$	$\dfrac{\$33 \div 5}{5\text{ hours} \div 5} = \dfrac{\$6.60}{1\text{ hour}}$ $= \$6.60\text{/hour}$

Find each unit rate.

1. 52 gallons of water for 5 fish   **$10\frac{2}{5}$ gal/fish**

2. typing 111 words in 2 minutes   **$55\frac{1}{2}$ words/min**

3. canoeing 49 miles in 4 days   **$12\frac{1}{4}$ mi/day**

4. a total weight of 78 pounds for 9 boxes   **$8\frac{2}{3}$ lb/box**

5. earning $350 for working 40 hours   **$8.75/hour**

6. An SUV can go 230 miles on one tank of gas. The gas tank holds 25 gallons. What is the SUV's gas mileage in miles per gallon?   **$9\frac{1}{5}$**

7. A messenger delivers 8 packages in 3 hours. At that rate, how many packages can she deliver in 15 hours?   **40 packages**

8–6

Name _____ Date _____

Reteach

Round Fractions

Round Up

If the numerator is almost as large as the denominator, round the number up to the next whole number.

Example: $\dfrac{9}{10}$ rounds to 1.

9 is almost as large as 10.

Round to $\frac{1}{2}$

If the numerator is about half of the denominator, round the fraction to $\frac{1}{2}$.

Example: $\dfrac{3}{5}$ rounds to $\dfrac{1}{2}$.

3 is about half of 5.

Round Down

If the numerator is much smaller than the denominator, round the number down to the previous whole number.

Example: $\dfrac{1}{5}$ rounds to 0.

1 is much smaller than 5.

Round each number to 0, $\frac{1}{2}$, or 1.

1. $\dfrac{9}{10}$ **1**   2. $\dfrac{1}{10}$ **0**   3. $\dfrac{5}{8}$ **$\dfrac{1}{2}$**

4. $\dfrac{2}{7}$ **$\dfrac{1}{2}$**   5. $\dfrac{9}{16}$ **$\dfrac{1}{2}$**   6. $\dfrac{1}{3}$ **$\dfrac{1}{2}$**

7. $\dfrac{2}{3}$ **$\dfrac{1}{2}$**   8. $\dfrac{6}{7}$ **1**   9. $\dfrac{4}{9}$ **$\dfrac{1}{2}$**

10. $\dfrac{5}{11}$ **$\dfrac{1}{2}$**   11. $\dfrac{1}{8}$ **0**   12. $\dfrac{7}{8}$ **1**

Answers (Lesson 8–6)

8-6 Skills Practice

Name _____ Date _____

Round Fractions

Round each number to 0, $\frac{1}{2}$, or 1.

1. $\frac{1}{12}$ **0**
2. $\frac{12}{13}$ **1**
3. $\frac{9}{18}$ **$\frac{1}{2}$**

4. $\frac{3}{4}$ **1**
5. $\frac{2}{9}$ **0**
6. $\frac{2}{3}$ **$\frac{1}{2}$**

7. $\frac{1}{2}$ **$\frac{1}{2}$**
8. $\frac{3}{8}$ **$\frac{1}{2}$**
9. $\frac{7}{8}$ **1**

10. $\frac{1}{8}$ **0**
11. $\frac{12}{15}$ **1**
12. $\frac{2}{9}$ **0**

13. $\frac{1}{4}$ **0**
14. $\frac{11}{12}$ **1**
15. $\frac{5}{6}$ **1**

16. $\frac{2}{16}$ **0**
17. $\frac{1}{3}$ **$\frac{1}{2}$**
18. $\frac{4}{5}$ **1**

19. $\frac{1}{8}$ **0**
20. $\frac{1}{5}$ **0**
21. $\frac{8}{9}$ **1**

Solve.

22. Mrs. Jones is putting up blinds to fit in a window opening that is $\frac{7}{8}$ yard wide. Should she round $\frac{7}{8}$ up or down when deciding on the size of blinds to purchase?

up

23. Marvin is mailing a copy of a document that is $12\frac{1}{8}$ inches long and $10\frac{1}{2}$ inches wide. Will the document fit in an envelope that is 12 inches long and $10\frac{1}{2}$ inches wide or in an envelope that is $12\frac{1}{2}$ inches long and 11 inches wide?

$12\frac{1}{2}$ inches long and 11 inches wide

8-6 Homework Practice

Name _____ Date _____

Round Fractions

Round each number to 0, $\frac{1}{2}$, or 1.

1. $\frac{1}{12}$ **0**
2. $\frac{5}{11}$ **$\frac{1}{2}$**
3. $\frac{3}{10}$ **$\frac{1}{2}$**

4. $\frac{8}{12}$ **1**
5. $\frac{2}{9}$ **0**
6. $\frac{14}{16}$ **1**

7. $\frac{6}{16}$ **$\frac{1}{2}$**
8. $\frac{7}{12}$ **$\frac{1}{2}$**
9. $\frac{3}{8}$ **$\frac{1}{2}$**

Solve.

10. Your basement has an $8\frac{3}{12}$ foot ceiling. To the nearest half foot, how tall is the tallest cabinet that can fit in the basement?

8 feet

11. Alice is giving a book as a gift that is $8\frac{3}{8}$ inches long and $6\frac{1}{12}$ inches wide. Will the book fit in a box that is $8\frac{1}{2}$ inches long and $6\frac{1}{2}$ inches wide or in a box that is 8 inches long and 6 inches wide?

$8\frac{1}{2}$ inches long and $6\frac{1}{2}$ inches wide

Spiral Review

Replace ◯ with < or > to make a true statement. (Lesson 8–5).

12. $\frac{3}{4}$ $\boxed{>}$ $\frac{1}{4}$
13. $\frac{4}{7}$ $\boxed{<}$ $\frac{5}{7}$

14. $2\frac{1}{9}$ $\boxed{>}$ $1\frac{2}{9}$
15. $1\frac{2}{3}$ $\boxed{<}$ $2\frac{1}{3}$

16. $\frac{9}{6}$ $\boxed{>}$ $\frac{5}{6}$
17. $3\frac{1}{12}$ $\boxed{>}$ $2\frac{11}{12}$

Answers

Answers (Lesson 8–6)

8–6

Name _____ Date _____

Enrich

Greatest Possible Error

When you measure a quantity, your measurement is more precise when you use a smaller unit of measure. But no measurement is ever exact–there is always some amount of error. The greatest possible error (GPE) of a measurement is one half the unit of measure.

unit of measure: $\frac{1}{8}$ inch

length of line segment: $1\frac{3}{8}$ inches

GPE: half of $\frac{1}{8}$ inch, or $\frac{1}{16}$ inch

Since $1\frac{3}{8} = 1\frac{6}{16}$, the actual measure of the line segment may range anywhere from $1\frac{5}{16}$ inches to $1\frac{7}{16}$ inches.

Use the GPE to give a range for the measure of each line segment.

1. $\frac{5}{8}$ in. to $\frac{7}{8}$ in.

2. $\frac{1}{4}$ in. to $\frac{3}{4}$ in.

3. $1\frac{7}{16}$ in. to $1\frac{9}{16}$ in.

4. 3.5 cm to 4.5 cm

5. Using this scale, the weight of a bag of potatoes is measured as 3 pounds. What is the range for the actual weight of the potatoes?

$2\frac{7}{8}$ lb to $3\frac{1}{8}$ lb

6. Using this container, the amount of a liquid is measured as 20 milliliters. What is the range for the actual amount of the liquid?

17.5 mL to 22.5 mL

Grade 5   37   Chapter 8

8–6

Name _____ Date _____

Problem-Solving Practice

Round Fractions

Solve.

1. A recipe for cookies calls for $\frac{3}{4}$ of a cup of chocolate chips. Should you buy a package with $\frac{1}{2}$ cup or a package with 1 cup?

1 cup

2. The cookie recipe also calls for $\frac{3}{8}$ of a cup of walnuts. Should you buy a package with 1 cup or a package with $\frac{1}{2}$ cup of walnuts?

$\frac{1}{2}$ cup

3. Your kitchen has a $9\frac{3}{4}$ foot ceiling. To the nearest half foot, what is the tallest refrigerator that can fit in the kitchen under a cabinet that hangs down 3 feet?

$6\frac{1}{2}$ ft

4. Russ is putting his photographs in an album that is $12\frac{1}{8}$ inches long and $10\frac{1}{2}$ inches wide. Should he trim the edges of the photographs to $12\frac{1}{2}$ inches long and 10 inches wide or to $12\frac{1}{2}$ inches long and $10\frac{1}{2}$ inches wide?

12 inches long and 10 inches wide

5. A farmer is planting squash plants that need $2\frac{3}{8}$ feet to spread out. He has an area along a fence that is 20 feet long. Round the amount of space the squash plants need to the nearest $\frac{1}{2}$ foot. How many squash plants can the farmer grow along the fence?

8 plants

6. Based on the area of his flowerbed, a gardener calculates that he needs $6\frac{8}{14}$ gallons of fertilizer. Should he round $6\frac{8}{14}$ up or down when deciding on the amount of fertilizer he should purchase?

up

Grade 5   36   Chapter 8

Chapter Resources

Answers (Lesson 8–7)

8-7 Reteach

Problem-Solving Investigation: Choose the Best Strategy

Fina did a survey of how much time students spend on homework each night. Out of 16 people interviewed, $\frac{1}{2}$ spend about 1 hour on homework and $\frac{1}{4}$ spend about 45 minutes on homework. The rest spend about 30 minutes on homework. How many students spend 30 minutes on homework?

Understand	$\frac{1}{2}$ of 16 students spend 1 hour on homework. $\frac{1}{4}$ of 16 students spend 45 minutes on homework. You need to know how many people spend 30 minutes on homework.
Plan	You can use the *act it out* strategy. Draw 16 students. Cross out the students who spend 1 hour and the students who spend 45 minutes on homework. You will be left with the students who spend 30 minutes on homework.
Solve	$\frac{1}{2}$ of 16 is 8. Cross out 8 students. $\frac{1}{4}$ of 16 is 4. Cross out 4 more students. Count the students that are left. 4 students spend about 30 minutes on homework.
Check	Use math to check your work. $16 - 8 - 4 = 4$ Your answer is correct.

8-7 Reteach

Problem-Solving Investigation (continued)

Use any strategy shown below to solve.

- Act it out
- Make a table
- Use logical reasoning
- Guess and check
- Work backward
- Solve a simpler problem

1. Out of the 200 students at Groves High, 50 spend 2 hours a night on homework, 25 spend 1 hour on homework, and 75 spend 45 minutes on homework. The rest spend 30 minutes on homework. How many students spend 30 minutes on homework?

    50 students

2. Mrs. Jones told her class of 30 students that 8 people scored 90 or above on a math test, 7 people scored between 80 and 89 and 10 people scored between 70 and 79. How many people scored lower than 70?

    5 people

3. If square tables are arranged in a restaurant so that only one person can sit on any side of the table, how many tables will it take to seat 40 people?

    10 tables

4. Alan bought a computer that was on sale for $568. If the computer originally cost $647, how much money did Alan save?

    $79

5. Forty people in a restaurant spend a total of $500. $\frac{1}{2}$ of the 40 people spend $20 each. What is the least amount of money each of the rest of the people spend?

    $5

Skills Practice — 8-7

Name _____ Date _____

Problem-Solving Investigation: Choose the Best Strategy

Use any strategy shown below to solve.

- Guess and check
- Make a table
- Work backward
- Use logical reasoning
- Solve a simpler problem
- Act it out

1. In how many ways can 5 people stand in line if one of the people always has to be first in line?

24 ways

2. The teacher told the class of 30 students that $\frac{1}{2}$ of them scored above an 80 on their math test. An additional $\frac{1}{3}$ of them scored at least a 70. How many of them scored below 70?

5 students

3. Alicia bought a CD player for $10 less than the regular price. If she paid $58 for the CD player, what was the regular price?

$68

4. Miguel bought boxes of chocolates. The first box weighed $4\frac{1}{4}$ pounds, the second, $2\frac{3}{4}$, and the third, $1\frac{1}{3}$. What is the total amount of chocolate that Miguel bought?

$8\frac{1}{3}$ pounds

5. After Miguel shared the chocolate with his friends, he had $3\frac{5}{8}$ pounds left. Then, he gave $2\frac{3}{4}$ pounds to his mother. Now, how much does he have?

$\frac{7}{8}$ pound

6. The first $\frac{1}{5}$ mile of a $\frac{3}{4}$-mile path through a rose garden is paved with bricks. How much of the path is not paved with bricks?

$\frac{11}{20}$ mile

Grade 5   40   Chapter 8

Homework Practice — 8-7

Name _____ Date _____

Problem-Solving Investigation: Choose the Best Strategy

Use any strategy shown below to solve.

- Guess and check
- Make a table
- Work backward
- Use logical reasoning
- Solve a simpler problem
- Act it out

1. Olivia bought a ring for $\frac{1}{2}$ off the regular price. If she paid $50, what was the regular price?

$100

2. Mrs. Jones told the class that $\frac{1}{3}$ of them scored 90 or above on the math test. Another $\frac{1}{3}$ of them had a passing score. What fraction of the class failed?

$\frac{1}{3}$ failed

3. At a park, a picnic shelter covers $\frac{1}{4}$ of an acre and a playground covers $\frac{5}{8}$ of an acre. How much area is covered by both the picnic shelter and the playground?

$\frac{7}{8}$ acre

4. Of the 300 students at school, 110 are in the chorus and 150 are in the band. Of these students, 50 are in both chorus and the band. How many students are neither in the chorus nor the band?

90 students

Round each fraction to 0, $\frac{1}{2}$, or 1.

5. $\frac{1}{7}$ **0**

6. $\frac{7}{8}$ **1**

7. $\frac{2}{10}$ **0**

8. $\frac{5}{6}$ **1**

9. $\frac{5}{9}$ **$\frac{1}{2}$**

10. $\frac{4}{10}$ **$\frac{1}{2}$**

Grade 5   41   Chapter 8

Answers (Lesson 8–7 and Vocabulary Test)

Name _____ Date _____

8 Vocabulary Test

Using the word bank below, complete each sentence by writing the correct word or words on the line provided.

improper fraction	numerator	denominator
fraction	mixed number	

1. The _____ is the number above the bar in a fraction; the part of the fraction that tells how many of the equal parts are being used.

1. numerator

2. A _____ has a whole number part and a fraction part.

2. mixed number

3. An _____ is a fraction that has a numerator that is greater than or equal to its denominator.

3. improper fraction

4. The bottom number in a fraction is the _____.

4. denominator

5. A number that represents part of a whole or part of a set is a _____.

5. fraction

Name _____ Date _____

8-7 Enrich

Choose the Operation

Solve.

1. A box is $\frac{1}{2}$ inch tall. If 5 of the boxes are stacked on top of each other, how tall is the stack of boxes?

$2\frac{1}{2}$ inches tall

2. Darlene needs $\frac{3}{4}$ yard of fabric to cover a chair. She has $\frac{3}{8}$ yard of fabric. How much more fabric does she need?

$\frac{3}{8}$ yard

3. Mr. Montgomery is a chef. He has created 250 new recipes. He plans to donate $\frac{3}{5}$ of them to the school library. How many recipes does he plan to donate?

150

4. The art department received a shipment of 6 boxes of clay. Each box weighed $\frac{3}{4}$ pound. How many pounds of clay were in the shipment?

$4\frac{1}{2}$ pounds

5. A sculptor has a steel tube that is $\frac{2}{3}$ foot long. To create a longer tube, he attaches it to another steel tube that is $\frac{5}{6}$ foot long. How long is the new steel tube?

$1\frac{1}{2}$ feet long

6. Marcel was in a triathalon, a race with 3 events. He ran 4 miles in $2\frac{1}{3}$ hour. He bicycled 5 miles in $\frac{3}{4}$ hour, and he swam 880 yards in $\frac{1}{2}$ hour. What was his total race time?

$1\frac{11}{12}$ hour or 1 hour 55 minutes

Answers

Name _____ Date _____

8 Oral Assessment

Draw 2 squares on the board. Divide each square into 4 equal parts. For the first square, shade in all sections. For the second square, shade in 1 section.

Read each question aloud to the student. Then write the student's answers on the lines below the question.

1. How many parts are shaded in the first square?

4

2. How many parts are shaded in the second square?

1

3. What is the fraction that represents the amount of parts shaded on the second square?

$\frac{1}{4}$

4. Tell how you got your answer.

There are four sections in all for the second square. Since only one section is shaded, the fraction is 1 over 4, or $\frac{1}{4}$

5. How would you write the total number of shaded squares as an improper fraction?

$\frac{5}{4}$

Name _____ Date _____

8 Oral Assessment *(continued)*

6. Tell how you got your answer.

Count the total number of shaded squares and write this number for the numerator. Count the number of sections in each box and write this number for the denominator.

7. How do you change this improper fraction to a mixed number?

Divide the numerator by the denominator. Write the remainder as a fraction with the divisor as the denominator.

8. What is this improper fraction as a mixed number?

$1\frac{1}{4}$

Draw 2 circles on the board. Divide each circle into 3 equal parts. For the first circle, shade in 2 sections. For the second circle, shade in 1 section.

9. How can you write the shaded portion of the first circle as a fraction?

$\frac{2}{3}$

10. How can you write the shaded portion of the second circle as a fraction?

$\frac{1}{3}$

11. Which fraction is larger?

$\frac{2}{3}$

Assessment

Chapter 8 Assessment Answer Key

Chapter Diagnostic Test
Page 44

1. $\dfrac{3}{8}$
2. $\dfrac{4}{9}$
3. $\dfrac{2}{3}$
4. 5
5. 5.5
6. 5
7. 3.29
8. $<$
9. $>$
10. $>$

Chapter Pretest
Page 45

1. $\dfrac{2}{3}$
2. $\dfrac{3}{5}$ gallon
3. $1\dfrac{2}{3}$
4. $1\dfrac{3}{4}$
5. $4\dfrac{2}{7}$
6. $\dfrac{9}{5}$
7. $\dfrac{19}{4}$
8. $\dfrac{25}{7}$
9. $>$
10. $<$
11. 1
12. $\dfrac{1}{2}$
13. 0
14. $\dfrac{2}{3}$ pound
15. 5 and 7

Quiz 1
Page 46

1. $\dfrac{2}{5}$ of a pizza
2. $\dfrac{1}{4}$ piece of paper
3. $\dfrac{1}{10}$ gal
4. $\dfrac{4}{7}$ foot
5. $1\dfrac{1}{2}$
6. $2\dfrac{2}{5}$
7. $3\dfrac{9}{13}$
8. $4\dfrac{1}{4}$
9. $1\dfrac{9}{11}$
10. $4\dfrac{1}{2}$

Answers

Chapter 8 Assessment Answer Key

Quiz 2
Page 47

Quiz 3
Page 48

Mid-Chapter Test
Page 49

Quiz 2 — Page 47

1. 7 students

2. 8 combinations

3. No

4. 4 hours

5. $\dfrac{15}{4}$

6. $\dfrac{21}{8}$

7. $\dfrac{13}{12}$

8. $\dfrac{93}{12}$

9. $\dfrac{11}{4}$

10. $\dfrac{41}{7}$

Quiz 3 — Page 48

1. $<$

2. $>$

3. $<$

4. $<$

5. 0

6. 1

7. $\dfrac{1}{2}$

8. 1

9. 3

10. 19 minutes

Mid-Chapter Test — Page 49

1. A

2. H

3. B

4. J

5. A

6. Divide the numerator by the denominator. Write the remainder as a fraction with the divisor as the denominator.

7. Multiply the whole number by the denominator. Add the numerator. Write the sum over the original denominator.

8. If the numerator is larger than the denominator, the fraction can be written as a mixed number.

9. $2\dfrac{1}{4}$

10. $\dfrac{23}{7}$

Chapter 8 Assessment Answer Key

Form 1
Page 55

1. _____C_____

2. _____J_____

3. _____A_____

4. _____G_____

5. _____D_____

6. _____H_____

7. _____B_____

8. _____F_____

Page 56

9. _____B_____

10. _____F_____

11. _____B_____

12. _____H_____

13. _____A_____

14. _____G_____

15. _____A_____

16. _____J_____

Form 2A
Page 57

1. _____B_____

2. _____F_____

3. _____C_____

4. _____J_____

5. _____C_____

6. _____F_____

7. _____B_____

8. _____H_____

(continued on the next page)

Answers

Chapter 8 Assessment Answer Key

Form 2A (*continued*)
Page 58

Form 2B
Page 59

Page 60

9. __D__

10. __F__

11. __D__

12. __G__

13. __B__

14. __G__

15. __A__

16. __J__

1. __D__

2. __F__

3. __A__

4. __F__

5. __B__

6. __H__

7. __B__

8. __H__

9. __D__

10. __G__

11. __A__

12. __J__

13. __B__

14. __G__

15. __D__

16. __J__

Chapter 8 Assessment Answer Key

1. $\dfrac{6}{7}$

2. $\dfrac{3}{7}$

3. **8 cuts**

4. **8 and 9**

5. $2\dfrac{2}{3}$

6. $5\dfrac{3}{10}$

7. $13\dfrac{4}{5}$

8. $3\dfrac{1}{3}$ **or** $\dfrac{10}{3}$

9. $\dfrac{2}{3}$

10. $\dfrac{47}{8}$

11. $\dfrac{11}{3}$

12. $\dfrac{139}{10}$

13. $<$

14. $>$

15. $<$

16. $>$

1. **12 cuts**

2. **4 and 5**

3. $3\dfrac{1}{2}$

4. $4\dfrac{5}{8}$

5. $37\dfrac{1}{2}$

6. $\dfrac{9}{10}$

7. $\dfrac{4}{10}$

8. $1\dfrac{2}{5}$ **or** $\dfrac{7}{5}$

9. $\dfrac{1}{2}$

(continued on the next page)

Answers

Chapter 8 Assessment Answer Key

Form 2D (*continued*)
Page 64

10. $\dfrac{38}{5}$

11. $\dfrac{61}{13}$

12. $\dfrac{53}{6}$

13. $>$

14. $<$

15. $<$

16. $<$

Form 3
Page 65

1. $31\dfrac{1}{3}$

2. $35\dfrac{1}{4}$

3. $4\dfrac{13}{14}$

4. no, she needs 3 yards of fabric

5. $\dfrac{10}{46}$ or $\dfrac{5}{23}$

6. $\dfrac{7}{6}$ or $1\dfrac{1}{6}$

7. $\dfrac{5}{3}$ or $1\dfrac{2}{3}$

8. $>$

9. $>$

Page 66

10. $\dfrac{38}{5}$

11. $\dfrac{103}{35}$

12. $\dfrac{296}{67}$

13. 9 cuts

14. 9 and 10

15. 36 and 49

16. $\dfrac{2}{11}$ or $\dfrac{20}{110}$

17. noon or 12:00 P.M.

18. 20 tables

Chapter 8 Assessment Answer Key

Page 67, Chapter Extended-Response Test
Scoring Rubric

Level	Specific Criteria
4	The student demonstrates a *__thorough understanding__* of the mathematics concepts and/or procedures embodied in the task. The student has responded correctly to the task, used mathematically sound procedures, and provided clear and complete explanations and interpretations. The response may contain minor flaws that do not detract from the demonstration of a thorough understanding.
3	The student demonstrates an *__understanding__* of the mathematics concepts and/or procedures embodied in the task. The student's response to the task is essentially correct with the mathematical procedures used and the explanations and interpretations provided demonstrating an essential but less than thorough understanding. The response may contain minor errors that reflect inattentive execution of the mathematical procedures or indications of some misunderstanding of the underlying mathematics concepts and/or procedures.
2	The student has demonstrated only a *__partial understanding__* of the mathematics concepts and/or procedures embodied in the task. Although the student may have used the correct approach to obtaining a solution or may have provided a correct solution, the student's work lacks an essential understanding of the underlying mathematical concepts. The response contains errors related to misunderstanding important aspects of the task, misuse of mathematical procedures, or faulty interpretations of results.
1	The student has demonstrated a *__very limited understanding__* of the mathematics concepts and/or procedures embodied in the task. The student's response to the task is incomplete and exhibits many flaws. Although the student has addressed some of the conditions of the task, the student reached an inadequate conclusion and/or provided reasoning that was faulty or incomplete. The response exhibits many errors or may be incomplete.
0	The student has provided a *__completely incorrect__* solution or uninterpretable response, or no response at all.

Answers

Chapter 8 Assessment Answer Key

Page 67, Chapter Extended-Response Test
Sample Answers

In addition to the scoring rubric found on page A27, the following sample answers may be used as guidance in evaluating open-ended assessment items.

1. a. A fraction is a number that names equal parts of a whole or parts of a group. A fraction represents division.

   b. The numerator is the number above the bar in a fraction. The denominator is the number below the bar in a fraction. The numerator tells how many parts of a whole are used. The denominator tells how many parts there are altogether.

2. $3\frac{1}{4}$ would round to 3 since it is closer to 3 on the number line.

3. a. First, divide the numerator (top number) by the denominator (bottom number). Write the remainder as the numerator on top of the old denominator. Write the quotient as the whole number.

$$\frac{7}{3} = 3\overline{)7} = 2 \text{ R1} \rightarrow 2\frac{1}{3}$$

   b. First, multiply the whole number by the denominator (bottom number). Add that sum to the numerator (top number). Write the final sum on top of the original denominator. Simplify if necessary.

$$2\frac{3}{4} = \frac{(2\times4) + 3}{4} = \frac{11}{4}$$

Chapter 8 Assessment Answer Key

Cumulative Test Practice Chapters 1–8

Page 68

Page 69

Page 70

8. ___F___

9. ___$\frac{5}{9}$___

10. ___23___

11. ___$\frac{24}{30}$ or $\frac{4}{5}$___

12. ___$\frac{3}{4} = \frac{6}{8}$___

3. ___C___

13. ___90___

4. ___G___

14. ___Randy___

5. ___A___

15. ___0.85___

16. ___5___

1. ___D___

2. ___H___

6. ___H___

7. ___C___

Answers